KEEP SWIMMING

Annaleise Easlea is a passionate
mental health advocate and veteran.

Annaleise spent the first six years of her
twenties tied to the Royal Australian Navy
and experienced severe depression both
during and after service.

Annaleise is now using her lived
experience to normalise mental health.
Her ability to hold space for others plays a
pivotal role in starting open conversations,
evoking change and providing compassion to
others. Once Annaleise started to share her
story and realised the impact it had on others,
Keep Swimming was born.

KEEP SWIMMING

REAL-LIFE STORIES TO HELP YOU FACE
THE WAVES OF MENTAL HEALTH

Annaleise Easlea

Thank you for being here. I would love to see how *Keep Swimming* has helped you.
Feel free to share with me by tagging @annaleise.easlea. You've got this x

www.keepswimmingbook.com

First published in 2023 by Annaleise Easlea

A catalogue entry for this book is available from the National Library of Australia.

ISBN: 978-1-922764-98-0

Printed by Ingram Spark
Book production by Publish Central
Illustrations by Ceri Bathgate @tropicoolstudio
Book Design by Veronica Steigner @fancy.pants.adventures
Cover Image and Book Photography by Marie Pfisterer @mariepfisterer
Author Photo by @itsjaclee
Poetry by Laury Houghton @lauryhoughton
Edited by Gail Tagarro @thebookwritingcoach

Stories by
Brenden Hall @brendenhall93 - Photo by @lukemarsdenphoto
Laury Houghton @lauryhoughton - Photo by @victoriarosevisuals
Kim Churchill @kimchurchill - Photo by @saskiaburmeister
Loz Lemons @sundaylemonade_ - Photo by @suzichadwickphotography
Ged Moriarty @gedm.oriarty
Shayelle Lajoie @shayellelajoie - Photo by @domgranger
Anton Nootenboom @thebarefoot_dutchman - Photo by @frankruiterphotographer
Courtney Welsh @lifewith_courtney_ - Photo by @josephinecarterphotography
Pharrell Shaymar @pharrell_shaymar - Photo by @justinphoto_melbourne

Disclaimer
The material in this publication is of the nature of general comment only, and does not represent professional advice or medical treatment. It is not intended to provide specific guidance for particular circumstances and it should not be relied on as the basis for any decision to take action or not take action on any matter which it covers. Readers should obtain professional advice where appropriate, before making any such decision. To the maximum extent permitted by law, the author and publisher disclaim all responsibility and liability to any person, arising directly or indirectly from any person taking or not taking action based on the information in this publication.

IT DOESN'T
MATTER HOW FAST
YOU MOVE

IT DOESN'T EVEN
MATTER WHAT
DIRECTION YOU GO

ALL THAT MATTERS
IS THAT YOU JUST
KEEP SWIMMING

IN MEMORY OF
DANIEL GARFORTH

23/01/1993 – 20/11/2014

YOUR LIGHT WILL
NEVER CEASE TO SHINE

FOR THE READER

Hey you.

I am so glad this book has found its way into your hands.

By picking it up, you have taken another step forward on your mental health journey, and that deserves to be celebrated. In fact, celebrate yourself every day. You are here, and every day that you find a way to keep going is a day worth celebrating.

I am so proud of you.

I want you to imagine you are in the water, and although the ocean is as smooth as glass when you first jump in, it is starting to get a bit rough out there. You keep treading water, but slowly, you start to lose your strength. You're struggling to keep afloat. Sounds like life sometimes, right? Well, this book is your lifebuoy, so grab it and hold on tight. Keep it close, take it to the beach, read it on the plane, pop it on your coffee table. Whatever you do, wherever you are, remember that this book is here for you. Together, we can keep swimming. Together, we can stay afloat.

To inspire you, nine incredible humans have shared their raw and honest experiences with mental health. We don't need to figure it all out from scratch. Sharing these stories might save you the pain and suffering of trying to navigate this journey on your own.

The lessons I have learnt on my own journey are spread throughout the pages of this book. These lessons have changed the way I think and feel, and have helped me on my darkest days. I hope they can help you too.

Be gentle on yourself. Take your time. Breathe.

Life is tough, but remember, so are you.

You've got this.

Annaleise x

PLEASE READ WITH CARE

This book contains themes of mental health, rape, self harm, and suicide.

Mental Health Helpline numbers are on Page 203.

CONTENTS

CHRONOLOGICALLY

STORIES

EMPOWERMENT PAGES

'You don't have
to just exist'

@annaleise.easlea

My Story

I WON'T LIE: WRITING ABOUT MY JOURNEY WITH MENTAL HEALTH HAS BEEN THE MOST CHALLENGING PART OF CREATING THIS BOOK. I DON'T QUITE KNOW HOW TO PUT THE HARDEST YEARS OF MY LIFE INTO WORDS, SO I'LL START BY PAINTING YOU A PICTURE.

On June 17, 2019, I discharged from the navy after six years of service. I was twenty-six. When you first join the military, they have to break you down so they can build you into exactly who they need you to be. But when you leave, after years of being conditioned, you don't get rebuilt into a civilian. You just go out into the world with years of experience behind you that very few would understand, trying to find your feet now that you've finally taken your boots off.

When I first left the navy, I thought that my hardest years were behind me. I had been so carried away with the thought of being free again that I never once expected that my mental health would decline further.

In August that year, I flew to Greece with my then-partner. We spent a month on the island of Ios, sipping sangria, jumping off rocks into crystal-clear waters and making friends with all the goats. It was on this trip that he dropped down on one knee and asked me to marry him. I had never thought about marriage before then, and I'd only had a small taste of my newfound freedom since leaving Defence. Despite all of that, I said yes, inevitably adding more confusion to my new life.

Now that you have a bit more insight, it's time to talk about what came next. My unravelling. I left the navy, I got engaged, I started a new job, I moved into a new area. I was going through the motions that those around me were going through. I was ticking boxes that society values so highly. On paper, it probably seemed like I had it all. The loving partner, the fantastic job, the promising future … but I couldn't shake the heaviness that began following me with every move I made. I couldn't quite put my finger on it, but something didn't feel right.

I would go to work and then spend my lunch breaks walking through the botanical gardens with a heavy cloud weighing me down. I was surrounded by beauty, yet all I could feel was my pain. As I walked, I would hold back tears with a lump in my throat and a tightness in my chest. I'd manage to get through the rest of the working day, only to break down the minute I walked through the front door at home. I would slump onto the couch and cry. It wouldn't be just a few tears here and there. Every night I would heave. My whole body would shake, and eventually I'd gather myself and head to bed, only to do it all again the following day. I didn't know why I felt like this. It was a slow but sure unravelling. It was the fall of Annaleise Easlea.

I didn't know who I was. I wasn't a sailor anymore. I was in the real world now, living a life that I couldn't identify with. I felt myself drifting further and further away. I'd thought I'd magically be happy after leaving the navy, but I could no longer remember what happiness felt like. Except for when I had a drink.

Drinking became an escape for me. It was the only time that I would light up. One sip and I would feel the heaviness ease and my world slowly start to look more enticing. One more sip, and I would feel elated, so I would continue drinking in an attempt to prolong the feeling. When I was drinking, I felt like I had found myself again. I'd forgotten what it was like to live in a world without feeling heavy every single day. I was drinking to get happy, and I loved it. It felt like a break from my depression … until the next day when the heaviness would creep back in, ten times more intense than before.

My life became a dance between being so deeply unhappy that I could no longer see the point of it, and drinking to feel something. This went on for over a year. During that time, I asked my fiancé for a break from our relationship so I could try and figure out what I needed. I didn't really learn anything except that it was even harder to make it through each day when I didn't have someone there holding my hand. So, after living apart for a short time, we moved back in together and set a date for the wedding: April 10, 2021.

Things got progressively worse, which makes complete sense as I wasn't being intentional with my life. I was just existing in a world I no longer wanted to be part of. Towards the end of 2020, I was going around in circles. I kept calling the wedding off. I couldn't imagine getting married when I didn't know who I was and hadn't felt genuine happiness for so long. How could I make someone else happy for the rest of their life if I couldn't even do it for myself? Again, despite it all, I decided to go ahead with the wedding.

I took a month off work at the start of 2021. I thought maybe all I needed was a break. I hired a van, went to Minjerribah (North Stradbroke Island) and stayed there for a week. I surfed every day, lounged in the sun, walked along the beaches every morning and read every night. This was the breaking point. I was doing all the things I used to love, yet I felt defeated. I had nothing left to give. I couldn't shake the heaviness. I couldn't control the thoughts that were consuming my mind. I was on the beach looking out at everyone in the surf, hearing the waves crashing and knowing that my world was crashing too. It wasn't just a case of me needing a break and then I'd be fine. It wasn't just a case of me leaving the navy and then I'd be happy. I needed something more. I needed help.

After what seemed like hours searching the internet for a psychologist, I made the call. I couldn't be seen until late February, so I booked the appointment and broke down straight after doing so. I had no idea how I would make it through the next couple of weeks. Once I got back to the mainland, I went straight to the doctors for the referral and to ask for antidepressants. After battling these feelings for over a year, I strongly felt that I needed something to get me through until my appointment. I was withering away. The doctor wouldn't prescribe me anything until I met with the psychologist. As soon as I got back to my car, I broke down again, the same words going over and over in my mind, 'I can't do this anymore.'

By that point, my mind had spiralled. I was thinking of suicide every single day. The more these thoughts entered my mind, the stronger they became. Every day, I would wake up and fight another battle in my head. I just wanted it to be over. I was done. My thoughts were dark, and they were real. I was ready to do whatever it took to stop the pain. I was so fortunate that my fiancé and my mum recognised this and took turns to make sure I wasn't left alone. With their constant and consistent support, I was able to make it to my first psychologist appointment.

I walked into the appointment a broken human, praying this would be exactly what I needed. My psychologist gave me an assessment to fill out and after going over the results, told me I was suffering from severe depression. I had scored off the charts. In the space of an hour, I was flagged as a high-risk patient. If I was late or didn't make a meeting, an ambulance would be called to my house. I had to schedule weekly appointments and create a safety plan. This solidified that there really was something going on. I wasn't just feeling sad, confused or unhappy. I was struggling to breathe.

It was only two months until our wedding. Two months to try and shift the feelings. Two months to try and lift the heaviness. Two months to try and feel genuine happiness once more, not the temporary happiness that I was finding in alcohol, which was creating absolute havoc with my heart and my head. My psychologist explained that I was using alcohol to self-medicate. To give myself the best chance, I needed to cut alcohol out, and I did.

I continued appointments with my psychologist and although I understood all of the tools and guidance she was giving me, I could not find the energy or will to apply them. I couldn't focus on doing what I knew would help when the pain was all-consuming. After a couple of weeks of seeing no improvement, we decided to start on antidepressants to help ease the depression so I could focus on doing on the work.

It was the combination of therapy and medication that worked for me. Slowly but surely, I started to feel a little lighter. I started to feel like I could breathe again. I started to have moments where I genuinely felt happy. It was the first time in three years that I felt I was becoming closer to myself. I kept going to my weekly appointments, and we put strategies in place to get through the wedding. On April 10, 2021, I got married. It was my amazing psychologist, the medication, support and hard work that made walking down the aisle possible.

It was the happiest day of my life. I was elated but most importantly, I felt like myself again. I was barefoot all day, and anyone who knows me well knows that means I was truly in my element. I had married my best friend. I was surrounded by family and friends who had travelled from all over the country to be there. I drank virgin pina coladas all day. I ate the most incredible vegan food and devoured the wedding cake. I danced all night long. It was pure magic and will be forever one of my most beautiful and cherished memories.

A month after the wedding, my mental health began declining rapidly. The heaviness crawled back in. It had made its way back despite my being so confident it was gone. I was back to where it all began—the suicidal thoughts, the breakdowns, the lack of will to keep going. My psychologist and I decided to switch antidepressants and, just like magic, it worked. I felt like myself once more, really happy, and in constant awe at the love for life that I had. My new normal became a fluctuation between being extremely happy with a few intense lows tossed in. Those low periods were more manageable than ever before because the heavy cloud had shifted, which allowed me to focus on the tools and strategies my psychologist had given me. After a couple of months of the good days outweighing the bad, I had another appointment with my psychologist and together, we decided I could go from having weekly appointments to booking in when I needed.

So we dropped back on the sessions and wrote up a mental health plan. We identified my triggers and warning signs. We worked on what I needed to prioritise in terms of self-care, and put in place strategies to move forward.

After nearly a year of seeing her, my psychologist was confident that I could do this. I could book in my sessions only when I needed them rather than scheduling them in advance. It felt like a breakup but in the best way. After the session, I cried tears of joy. I was so proud of myself that I was finally at a point where I could be out in the world again. I could be social. I could set boundaries, and I could take time for myself. Above all, I could remember what it was like to feel happy and not have to mask how I was truly feeling.

I got through a couple of weeks, but as quickly as I'd broken up with my psychologist, I had to go back in to see her. I had the worst breakdown I'd had in months. I was driving when it happened. I couldn't shake the feelings or thoughts. I was trembling, crying uncontrollably, unable to see where I was going and ended up hitting the curb. I couldn't think straight. This went on for another week. In the past, I would have delayed seeking help, but I knew what this was. I knew I was spiralling. I called my psychologist and booked in an appointment. We unpacked the triggers that had sparked the decline. I spent more time alone to reflect on what was flooding my mind and worked out which steps I needed to take next.

The time spent alone led me to realise that I was struggling with identity. I was living a life that I didn't align with. I was living someone else's dream, not mine. I had never really given myself a chance to figure out who I was outside of Defence. I had jumped from one institution (Defence) straight into the next (marriage). I had never stopped to find out who Annaleise Easlea was at her core. I had to dig deep and ask myself the tough questions. Was this life bringing me joy? Was it serving me? What would I do if it didn't matter what anybody thought? I found the answers I needed, mustered all the courage I could find and left my marriage nine months after entering it.

I finally listened to myself. I used to place so much value on the thoughts, opinions and judgements of others, but once I put my needs higher than theirs, I was able to walk away from some massive chapters of my life and venture towards new ones that were more aligned with me. I was listening to my gut. I made decisions that felt right for me.

I even weened myself off the antidepressants and felt more at peace than ever before. I started to appreciate my life–the beautiful mess that it is.

I was finally on my way to learning who I was without Defence forming part of my identity, without being in a marriage, without feeling like an imposter in my own world.

Some choices I have made haven't been right for me, while others have been spot-on. This is life in a nutshell. We have to try different things, make different choices and take different paths from time to time. We won't always know if it's going to be good for us until we give it a go, but we have to try.

I know I'm on the right path now. Despite the pain and suffering of the past three years, despite going through a separation and losing the life I had, despite losing the support of my family and losing my financial independence, I would do it all over again to get to where I am now. It's not always easy, but it is possible. I was so close to leaving this world before I ever truly allowed myself to live in it. Yet here I am, writing these words. I am so glad I am still here. It is clear to me now that I didn't want my life to end, I just wanted the pain to stop. I found out how to keep swimming, and I know you can too.

The one thing that stayed constant through the toughest period of my life was my ability to ask myself, 'What do I need?' I ask myself this question every single day. Some days it will be a walk, and other days it will be some form of connection. Some days it will be a divorce, and other days it will be a hug. So when you're feeling like the world is falling on top of you, stop and ask yourself, 'What do I need?' Then do it. You know yourself better than anyone else.

To get through every day, I always call on everything I learnt during my sessions with my psychologist. I call on the things that truly make my heart feel free. I spend most of my time alone, and I've learnt to absolutely love that. I know now that I cannot depend on anyone but myself for my happiness, so I spend my days making my mind and my world a place I want to be. You can do the same.

It's going to get hard, but if you have your own back, the universe will too. It is important to remember that nothing changes if nothing changes. So don't be afraid to make a change if you feel it's right for you. You are the designer of your life. Anything is possible. You don't have to stay stagnant. You don't have to stay in a job, a relationship or a place that doesn't light you up. You don't have to just exist. You don't have to feel like it's over before it's ever really begun. You can choose to LIVE. Listen to the whispers, listen to your gut. What do YOU want?

Life is beautiful. When it all feels like a mess, just remember that sometimes your life has to crumble so your soul can shine through the cracks and you can start to rebuild your world with more colour and beauty than ever before.

27

"WHEN YOU'RE TIRED
LEARN TO REST NOT QUIT"
- BANKSY -

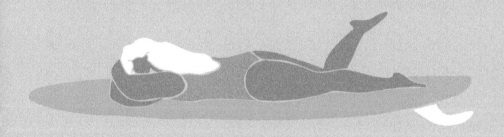

Like the trees in fall,

I have lost my leaves.

I feel vulnerable and bare,

But remain firmly grounded.

I know that just as time will pass,

And seasons will change,

I will heal.

My leaves will grow back,

And I will be full of life once again.

LAURY HOUGHTON

Focus on the next step

not the whole staircase

QUESTION YOUR THOUGHTS

One of the most powerful tools that my psychologist gave me was to question my own thoughts. During our sessions, I would explain how I was feeling or what I was thinking. My psychologist would then, ever so calmly, question the thoughts I was having. Were they an accurate representation of my life or was my mind running wild?

By having someone else question my thoughts, I gradually learnt how to question them on my own. In between our sessions, if I started to feel like it was becoming too much, I learnt to stop and check in with myself. I would ask myself these three questions:

WHAT ARE THE FEELINGS OR THOUGHTS I AM HAVING?

ARE THESE FEELINGS OR THOUGHTS HELPFUL?

WHAT CAN I DO TO HELP MYSELF RIGHT NOW?

By using these questions as journal prompts, I was able to get my thoughts out of my head and onto paper. I was able to look at them and determine if they were helpful to me. If they weren't, I would decide what would help me instead and do it. I discovered how to get out of my head and turn my thoughts into an action. I was able to really check in with myself, determine what I needed in that moment and act on it. I even started to jot down multiple actions that would help me and cross them off as I worked through them. This helped to free myself of the power that depression had over me. It helped me take back control of myself and my mind.

This process has been pivotal in my journey. Every time I feel like I'm being dragged down by the weight of my thoughts and feelings, I write these questions in my journal and find a way to keep going.

HOW TO KEEP SWIMMING

When you're feeling like you can't escape the madness in your mind, grab a journal and a pen. Take a moment. Breathe. Write it all down. Ask yourself, 'Are these feelings or thoughts helping me?' Chances are they probably aren't. Now is your opportunity to ask yourself what would be helpful instead. What can you do right now to help yourself? You can use the lessons and stories throughout this book to inspire you when considering what you can do to help yourself. By asking yourself these questions you can turn your thoughts into an action, then close the book and start swimming.

It's important to remember that this is not the single tool, or the most important tool, but a tool that you can use when there is a day or moment that you are struggling with. Remember that YOU are in control, don't let your thoughts control you.

There will be some days when you can only do the bare minimum and that is completely okay. Just remember, *'It doesn't matter how fast you move. It doesn't even matter what direction you go. All that matters is that you just keep swimming.'*

"WHEN A FLOWER DOESN'T BLOOM YOU FIX THE ENVIRONMENT IN WHICH IT GROWS NOT THE FLOWER"

-ALEXANDER DEN HEIJER-

My friend has two gardens, one on the left side of her driveway and one on the right. There is a lavender bush planted in each. The lavender bush in the left garden flourished! It stood tall and had an abundance of lavender. But the lavender bush in the right garden struggled.

So my friend dug it up and replanted it in the left garden. Slowly but surely, it started to grow, and more lavender appeared. It went on to blossom into the most beautiful bush.

Nature is one of our biggest teachers. This is a little reminder that if you are struggling, feeling a bit stagnant and not able to grow, then take a step back and assess your environment. Perhaps, like the lavender bush, a little change in your environment can help you to flourish and bloom too.

ABSOLUTELY EVERYTHING
TAKES TIME

BE CAREFUL NOT
TO COMPARE
YOUR
CHAPTER ONE
TO SOMEONE ELSE'S
CHAPTER TEN

'I am worth more
than my medals'
@brendenhall93

Brenden Hall

BRENDEN IS A PARALYMPIC, WORLD AND COMMONWEALTH GAMES CHAMPION. AT JUST SIX YEARS OLD, HIS RIGHT LEG WAS AMPUTATED AFTER COMPLICATIONS FROM CHICKEN POX. THIS NEVER STOPPED HIM. BRENDEN HAS BEEN A HIGH-PERFORMANCE ATHLETE IN SWIMMING FOR THE LAST FIFTEEN YEARS AND IS NOW A FIRST-TIME DAD TO BODHI AND WINSTON (THE PUG).

43

Mental health is a large part of high-performance sport. As athletes we are expected to get up and go, to compete at our absolute peak whenever called upon. If you're not mentally ready to go, you are left behind. Competition is a high-pressure environment and although we are given many tips and tricks to try and remain as calm and relaxed as possible, it doesn't always work. We tend to experience the highest highs and the lowest lows just from doing something we love. Over the last few years I've had a heavy personal experience with this.

In 2019, I competed at the World Para Swimming Championships in London. For the first time in my life, I experienced what was to me failure. I'd pulled on the green and gold along with the expectations upon myself to get in and get the job done, win the gold medal in my main event (S9 400m Freestyle)—for me, my family, my country and more importantly my team. I was beaten for the first time in ten years by a finger. I hated myself. I had failed myself and everyone around me. I promised myself that I'd never 'lose' again. From that moment on after returning home, having a break and going on my honeymoon, I made sure that I would throw absolutely everything on the line to win. I would make sure my body felt like hell and push myself so I was constantly sore to show myself that I was doing the work. All to make sure that when it came to racing in Tokyo 2020, I had all the money in the bank.

Everything was going swell, and I was feeling and looking fitter than I'd ever been in my entire career, achieving swimming times I hadn't swum for ten years. Then along came COVID, the global pandemic that officially stopped the world. We persevered with assurances that the games were going ahead, until they weren't. For all of us athletes it was a hard blow. Some of us were potentially looking at a final games before considering retirement. But like the rest of the world we slowed down, took a breath and dug deep, being resilient and finding ways to adapt. Many athletes including me really struggled with the lockdowns because we hate sitting still. While the world around us slowed and stopped, I took this time to focus on my studies for a little while. I looked for ways to continue to move and get the most out of my body until I found a routine I enjoyed outside the pool. Eventually, we realised we'd still get the same opportunity but a year later. We all hung on, determined to make sure the dream stayed alive and we'd get the job done when Tokyo came round in 2021.

I'd done it, I had pushed through and there I was in Tokyo, about to defend my Paralympic title. I'd been dreaming of this moment for the last five years since I'd stepped off the dais in Rio. Everything about my preparation told me I was going to perform one of the greatest races I ever had. I ended up swimming one of the best times I had in five years but at the cost of coming fourth in my main event. It hit me straightaway. Thoughts of, 'Fuck, I'm too old for this. I'm fucking done.' Then once I was out of the pool and putting my prosthetic leg on, the realisation that I had failed again really hit me. From that point on the thoughts got worse. Everything I'd been doing for the past eighteen months felt like a complete and utter waste. I told my coach, 'This isn't right, I'm a fucking failure.' I failed everyone back home who is supporting me. Especially my wife and my family who'd sacrificed so much over the years. I don't belong on this team. I'm not worthy enough to be on this team swimming for Australia. I'm fucking worthless. I wanted to go home. I didn't want to talk to anyone. Because of this mentality, the rest of my Games campaign suffered and I had the worst meet of my life. There were moments when I was on my own and I didn't want a bar of anything or anyone and constantly tried to hold tears back. As quick as my Tokyo Paralympic experience started, I wanted it done and I just wanted to fucking vanish.

How did you keep swimming?

As an athlete, my support crew helped me in my darkest moments. This includes my wife, my coach, my family, my best mates, my teammates, and other athletic staff such as our psychologist. They lend you an ear. They do their best to help draw it out of you. They offer the constant reminder that you are not alone. They always helped to ground me and remind me of why I swam in the first place—for the pure enjoyment and love of being in the water. My wife, my coach and my roommate/best mate reminded me that swimming isn't everything. The number of medals around your neck does not determine your self-worth.

How I had made an impact on people's lives, how I behaved as a person and how I held myself were more important. By creating strong, long-lasting relationships with these people I'd had a greater effect than by winning a medal. Life is much more than just about swimming. It might be my life now. It may have been in the past, but I have to remember that I'm not going to swim forever and there are more important things out there. That's what these people really helped me understand. I rediscovered my self-worth. I actually did mean something and I mattered.

What do you do when you notice your mental health declining?

I've learnt to start conversations when I notice my mental health declining. It might be with my wife, my family, my mates, my coach or my psych. It's simply finding the right person at the right time who I feel comfortable having the conversation with. Sometimes it is easiest to do this with someone who has an outside perspective and doesn't spend a whole lot of time with me. It's times like these that I found the team psych most useful. It's about chatting with someone who will help you find the right perspective and remind you of the important things in life.

When I've managed to have a good chat and get it all out, the easiest way to improve my mental health is through movement. I don't care what sort of movement as long as it's something. A swim, a surf, a solid workout or something as simple as a walk with loved ones goes a really long way. It gets all the good juices flowing again and feeling good. Top that off with a quality feed and coffee and the mental health starts to go up and up from there. I need to be continually surrounded by the right people and avoid those lonesome moments because that's when it gets tough.

What advice would you give to someone struggling with their mental health?

Everyone's experience with mental health is so different and there are so many ways to seek and offer guidance during those tough times. There's not one specific lock and key combination that works for everyone.

The best advice I can offer is to find what you're comfortable with and that works for you. Sometimes it's a matter of trial and error for what helps you to improve your mental health. I know that's how it worked for me and how I've managed to find that balance. You need a balance both physically and mentally, for you alone. Learn to be a little bit selfish and put yourself first for a while instead of trying to make others happy. Surround yourself with people who allow this and support you no matter what.

It's important to set little goals for yourself. For me, public speaking and public engagement is a big part of what I do. When I was going through my darkest times, I thought I was an embarrassment to be offering insight and advice to future generations of hard-working people. After working through it with the help of the psychologist, I slowly reintroduced myself to these environments. I started off with small groups of people and shared my journey of how I had ended up here and how I considered myself not worthy to speak to them. This sort of sharing and feedback helped boost my confidence and reminded me that I was capable and worthy. It's now my goal to get back to full public speaking and sharing my journey and life struggles, both physical and mental, with anyone who will listen. Find something that is important to you and set yourself small goals. It could be something as simple as getting up and making your bed or going for a daily walk. Other than that, find what works best for you and be open to any ideas that come your way.

47

DON'T
BE ASHAMED
OF YOUR
STORY

FOR ONE DAY
IT WILL INSPIRE
OTHERS

YOU ARE NOT
YOUR EMOTIONS

Happy seems to be the pinnacle of all the emotions available to us. There is such a range of human emotion and yet, happy seems to hold the most value. We place so much pressure on ourselves to be happy. When I was in the thick of my depression, I felt defeated if I didn't feel happy in moments when I 'should'. Looking back, I was putting too much pressure on myself to feel and behave a certain way. By striving so desperately to be happy and being so disappointed when I wasn't, I was subconsciously telling myself that it was not okay to feel other emotions.

I wanted to start recognising and acknowledging that all emotions are valid and valuable. **We will feel and experience other emotions.** This is an undeniable truth of the human experience. It's unrealistic for us to think we can achieve a constant state of happiness. My goal was to adjust my thinking and allow myself to feel my other emotions without ignoring or denying them.

I no longer wanted to feel guilty or upset for not being happy. Instead, I wanted to accept that it was okay to feel other emotions. Instead of striving to be happy, I learnt how to be content with feeling whatever emotion was presenting itself. I learnt that **it is okay to be sad. It is okay to be angry. It is okay to NOT be happy.**

HOW TO KEEP SWIMMING

To be happy all the time is not realistic. But it *is* realistic to feel emotions, accept them and sit with them. All emotions serve a purpose. Being happy isn't the goal. Being okay with whatever you're feeling is.

Take some time to imagine your neighbour knocking on your door. You don't want to deal with them in that moment, so you ignore the knock and pretend you aren't home. However, they know you're inside, so they keep coming back, knocking louder and louder each time. Eventually, you have to open the door.

Emotions are the same. If we ignore them, they don't magically disappear. They will build up and come back with more force and impact than before. So instead, it is always a good idea to answer that door and acknowledge your emotions. When you do, you remove the power they have over you.

You can start by paying attention to the way you think or speak about your feelings. You are not sad; rather, you are feeling sad. You are not angry; rather, you are feeling angry. You are not surprised, rather, you are feeling surprised. See what I did there? By switching 'I am X' with 'I am feeling X' you are reaffirming that the emotions you feel DO NOT define you. **You are not your emotions.** For example:

I AM ANGRY switch to I AM FEELING ANGRY

I AM HAPPY switch to I AM FEELING HAPPY

I AM DEPRESSED switch to I AM FEELING DEPRESSED

I AM ANXIOUS switch to I AM FEELING ANXIOUS

These simple switches to our emotional language tie in with Dr Dan Siegel's concept of 'Name it to tame it.' When we name the emotion(s) we are feeling, we are hitting pause and allowing our brain to stop and make sense of the situation. It gives us the time and space we need to determine how to respond.

Next time you find yourself having a moment where your emotions are knocking on your door, ask yourself, 'What emotion am I feeling?' Name the emotion out loud. State 'I am feeling X.' If you're struggling to identify exactly what you're feeling, turn to the next page and use the Feeling Wheel by Gloria Willcox to find the emotion that resonates with you the most in that moment.

By simply identifying and naming what we're experiencing, we become more in tune with our emotions and can work towards managing them better. We are no longer ignoring them. We are acknowledging them and remaining in control of the situation rather than letting our emotions control us.

53

THE FEELING WHEEL

It can often be difficult to describe how we are feeling. Use this Feeling Wheel to help you find the best words.

1) Start from the centre of the wheel

2) Have a look at the core emotions and see if you can best identify the emotion that you are feeling

3) Work your way outwards to find another word to better describe how you are feeling

4) You can also scan over the wheel and notice which words you resonate with the most in this moment

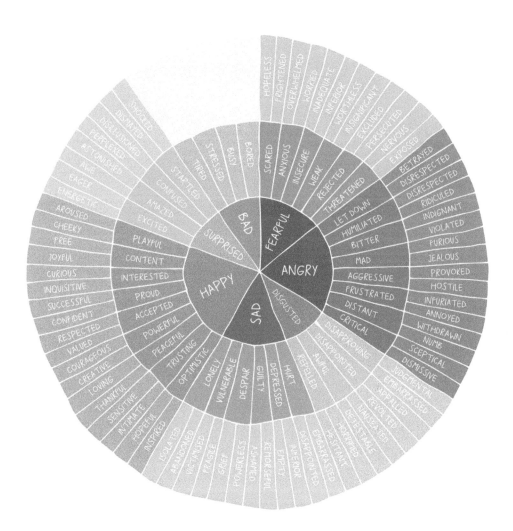

THE FEELING WHEEL
CREATED BY GLORIA WILLCOX
TRANSACTIONAL ANALYSIS JOURNAL 1 OCT 1982
TAYLOR & FRANCIS
REPRINTED BY PERMISSION OF THE PUBLISHER
(TAYLOR & FRANCIS LTD, HTTP://WWW.TANDFONLINE.COM)

TAKE
A BREAK
THE WORLD
CAN WAIT

Sometimes, your world will flip upside down. Sometimes, the walls might start to crumble around you. Sometimes, you will feel the deepest of pain and despair. And sometimes, your life will just be downright messy.

In those moments when you feel like there is nowhere left to turn, remember that butterflies were once piles of goo wrapped in a blanket before they could finally spread their wings.

We all, humans and animals alike, go through these uncomfortable yet transformative stages.

These moments are when the biggest growth happens. It is okay if it feels uncomfortable. Growth often occurs as you're moving through unfamiliar territory. Just keep going.

When you make it through, and you WILL make it through, you can break free of your cocoon, spread your wings and FLY.

'Writing gave me the power
to be in control of my story'

@lauryhoughton

Laury Houghton

LAURY IS A CREATIVE FROM BEAUTIFUL NEW ZEALAND A MOTHER AND AN EMPATH. LAURY IS VENTURING THROUGH THIS WORLD AS THE STRONGEST VERSION OF HERSELF AFTER SHE FOUND SOLACE IN PUTTING PEN TO PAPER AND TURNING HER THOUGHTS INTO POETRY

For longer than I would like to admit, my physical appearance has ruled my life. I have had a toxic and damaging relationship with my body since a young age. I recall being bullied in primary school for being too hairy, and then bullied again only a year later for shaving my legs. I remember taking photos in sepia on my pink flip phone, wearing a little too much eyeliner and a low-cut top, to post online. I remember carefully tearing out the pages of magazines to cover my walls with the faces and bodies of celebrities I desired to look like.

I joined a talent agency at sixteen, where I was told that I was a 'conventional beauty' and therefore I wouldn't get many modelling jobs. I wasn't tall or skinny enough to fit the criteria for most of the jobs that circulated. When it was suggested that I enter a beauty pageant, I did. After going home as 'Miss Photogenic', I felt deflated.

On the way home, as I rubbed my aching feet, I wondered whether I just wasn't pretty enough.

My desire for perfectionism meant that I was constantly seeking external validation. My worth was measured by how others perceived me. This grew into fierce anxiety and depression.

My anxiety prevented me from enjoying social situations, as I was constantly worried about what others were thinking about me. I desired attention online where I could control how I was seen, but dreaded attention in real-life situations. The hours leading up to a social event would have me sick to my stomach, playing out the different scenarios in my head as I chose the perfect outfit and applied enough makeup to make me feel good about myself. Many of my panic attacks occurred in the hours before spending time with others, or after a social interaction that I felt hadn't gone perfectly.

My anxiety made my relationships extremely difficult as I was never able to be completely myself. I placed high expectations on my partner and became frustrated when he did not fit the perfect image I desired.

My depression arose from the constant disappointment of not being perfect. Each time I did not meet my expectations, a little part of my light dimmed. My perception of myself was very warped and my entire life became a dark place that I resented.

Having such a low sense of self-worth and minimal self-respect put me in a very vulnerable position in relationships. I allowed myself to be manipulated and abused in order to be liked. I was surrounded by the wrong kind of friends and sought attention from people who did not respect me.

One day, something inside of me changed and I finally started to realise my worth. Since that moment I have been on a mission to become the best and most authentic version of myself, no longer striving to be perfect or worrying about what others think. It has been the most freeing decision I ever made, after realising that the only person expecting me to be perfect was myself.

How did you keep swimming?

My saviour was poetry. By putting pen to paper I allowed all of the pent-up thoughts and emotions to flow from inside my head to outside my body.

Writing poetry allowed me to express and release emotions in a way that was private, and therefore felt safe. I was not yet ready to talk with anyone about what I was feeling, or what I had experienced.

I found there was magic in turning unpleasant thoughts and experiences into art; making something ugly into something beautiful. Writing also gave me the power to be in control of my own story. I held the pen and therefore I had control of the narrative and, ultimately, how it ended.

I never intended to share my poetry, although when I eventually did, it changed my life. Through sharing my innermost thoughts and struggles, I connected with others in a way that I did not realise was possible. I was reassured to learn that many others had the same or similar experiences and felt comforted by my words.

What do you do when you notice your mental health declining?

I now have an appreciation that there cannot always be sunshine and that there will be dull days.

On dull days, I create my own sunshine, whether it be putting on some music that feels good, having a long shower, or moving my body in the fresh air. I never rely on others to make me feel better anymore.

If my emotions feel complex, or my thoughts are heavy, I continue to use poetry as a form of release. I scribble notes on my phone, or sit down with a journal and empty my head. Processing these thoughts and emotions is crucial for me to ensure that my mental health does not decline.

What advice would you give to someone struggling with their mental health?

Find your own way of releasing and processing the thoughts and emotions that are weighing you down. You will likely feel heavy if you keep them inside your head. If you don't feel safe sharing them aloud yet, try writing them down somewhere private.

Create your own sunshine! Find simple things that make you feel good and make time for them. It doesn't have to be grand or expensive, in fact, the simpler and easier the better. And most importantly, never rely on anyone else to make you feel good.

HOW YOUR LIFE FEELS TO YOU
IS FAR MORE
IMPORTANT THAN HOW IT LOOKS
TO SOMEONE ELSE

Have an early night
Call a friend
Eat some fruit
Swim in the ocean
Go for a walk
Dance in your living room
Breathe with intention
Read a book
Stretch like a cat
Watch the clouds pass
Move your body
Wash your face
Take a break
Reach out for help
Get some sunshine
Write a letter to yourself

Whatever it is, take care of yourself today.

If you're not feeling great,
try and do just one thing that would benefit you.

Sometimes the smallest action
can make the biggest difference.

Remember, tough times don't last but tough people do.
And you, my friend, are tough.

"The quality of your life is determined by the quality of questions you ask yourself on a daily basis"

Tony Robbins

EMPOWER YOURSELF

One of the most profound tools we have is the ability to question ourselves using quality questions.

In life, when we are faced with something that causes us pain, we often ask ourselves questions that aren't truly helpful at all. Questions like:

WHY?

WHY ME?

WHY IS THIS HAPPENING TO ME?

WHY CAN'T I CATCH A BREAK?

These questions disempower us. Instead of learning and growing from the situation or experience , they allow us to stay stuck and contribute further to our downward spiral.

Your history shows that you've survived 100% of the situations you've been through, so don't be afraid to take back the reins and ask yourself the tough questions. Through the quality of your questions, you can turn your trials into teachings.

To take back the power, we can change the foundation of our questions and ask WHAT or HOW instead of dwelling on the WHY. By asking different questions, we get different answers. By getting different answers, we think differently. By thinking differently, we can learn or grow from the situation.

HOW TO KEEP SWIMMING

When you next catch yourself ruminating on those negative thoughts that creep into your mind, **always choose to empower yourself** with questions like:

WHAT CAN I LEARN FROM THIS?

WHAT IS THIS TEACHING ME?

WHAT CAN I DO TO CHANGE THE WAY I FEEL ABOUT THIS?

WHAT CHANGES CAN I MAKE?

WHAT STEPS CAN I TAKE TODAY THAT WILL BENEFIT ME?

WHAT DO I NEED TODAY?

WHAT CAN I DO IN THE NEXT 24 HOURS THAT WILL HELP ME?

HOW CAN I IMPROVE?

HOW CAN I BECOME THE BEST VERSION OF MYSELF?

These types of questions give you more space to explore how you think and feel, and the answers you find will help you learn. Give yourself space to dive into these questions more. Watch yourself grow.

Here is your reminder that there are going to be periods in your life that are the absolute pits. These times will be uncomfortable, but you have to remember that that is where the growth happens.

When I first jumped on the plane to travel to Sri Lanka by myself, I felt like a fish out of water, way out of my depth. It was uncomfortable; it didn't feel natural to me at all. But now, because of pushing through those uncomfortable feelings, I have grown so much and am a better person today.

So, when certain aspects
of my life test me, I know that
these are the times where
I can grow the most, and you
can too. Lean into those
feelings and slowly allow
yourself to trust the process.

If you have trouble doing that,
remember that we literally
put cow shit on soil to help
plants grow. So when some
shit is sprinkled on your life,
remember that it isn't there to
harm you, it is there to help
you grow.

'I found calm within
the whirlwind'
@kimchurchill

Kim Churchill

KIM IS AN AUSTRALIAN FOLK AND BLUES SINGER, SONGWRITER AND MUSICIAN. ONSTAGE, KIM PERFORMS MAGICALLY, TREATING HIS AUDIENCE THROUGH HIS VOICE, GUITAR, HARMONICA, DRUMS AND PERCUSSION. OFFSTAGE, KIM USES AN INCREDIBLE AMOUNT OF DISCIPLINE TO FIND HIS BALANCE AND NURTURE HIS MENTAL HEALTH THROUGH GRATITUDE, MEDITATION AND MOVEMENT.

As I type these first words, I'm sitting in the passenger seat of my friend's ute, broken down on the side of a road about two hours out of Exmouth in Western Australia. I'm a travelling musician, heading south for some radio and TV interviews in Perth. It's a fitting place to begin this little story. As I sit here, with very little to do, no reception and no idea how long it will take for help to come, I feel a gentle but barely noticeable anxiety starting in the middle of my chest. I've got a day and a half still to get to Perth. There's time. But I start thinking, what else might go wrong? How much time will this take? How much money is it going to cost? As is often the case as a touring musician, there are no answers for now. Most of the situation is out of my control.

When something like this happens it's triggering. It takes me back to many traumatic experiences over the past thirteen years of touring where things have gone drastically wrong. It's like a fight or flight switch that seems to get stuck in the 'on' position and it can be very challenging to come out of. When things like this go wrong, the anxious part of me that struggles to shut down feels justified to stay on and in high alert.

One of the wildest parts of my job is the fact that, several hours earlier, I was tucking into an amazing breakfast after a beautiful sunrise hike from the glamping/fine dining retreat I had been staying at for free courtesy of a friend who came to my Exmouth gig. I was on an incredible high. The gig had been fantastic. The community had taken me in and I felt deeply at home. I'd been in town for three beautiful, laughter-filled days and felt I could spend the rest of my life in this perpetual state of joy.

It's the highs and lows of life as a touring musician that are the wild part. It's a beautiful, fun, adventurous existence, but it stretches your emotional capacity in every direction. One second you have adoration and love and success heaped upon you. The next, you're forgotten or broke, or you're broken down on the side of the highway.

When I first tried to perform, it was a very negative experience. I was so scared and nervous. I'd shake and feel sick and wish with all my might that the performance would already be done and that I could get back to my life. I'd seize up onstage and couldn't play simple songs or parts. It was consistently an awful experience for quite a while. My friend's older brother would buy me beers that I'd pack in my bag when my folks took me to little gigs or classical guitar exams. When no one was watching I'd race out to the car and skull a couple of warm VBs to take the edge off. I was around fourteen or fifteen at the time. The alcohol numbed the intensity of the emotional response to going onstage. But over time, and with lots of positive experiences, I grew comfortable onstage and started to really enjoy myself. Playing music for people became a beautiful part of my life. It has taken me all over the world and I've experienced so much love and gratification.

I realised that you can be positively stressed, when stress is wrapped in beautiful layers of excitement, laughter, love and feelings of abundance, success and confidence.

I was very lucky in my first few years as a musician. I come from a small town, Merimbula, on the far south coast of NSW, Australia. On our way to the Sydney Conservatorium, where I was sitting my final classical guitar exam in my last year of high school, I explained to Mum my dream to live in a campervan and busk all over the country. Mum loved it and got so excited we checked out some car yards, found a beautiful high-top Toyota HiAce and Mum took out a loan so we could buy it that day. It was an incredible feeling. I had my own van! A mate's dad who was a carpenter helped me build it into a beautiful little home. I was busking every day to pay Mum off. As soon as I could, I hit the road and started playing everywhere. I was young and full of confidence and dreams with a big smile on my face and a wild spirit. People loved it and I found that entertaining crowds came easily to me.

My career gathered momentum and soon I was playing forty-date tours of America, Canada and Europe. I had major record labels throwing deals and money at me and telling me I was going to be a big deal. They loved me before they even knew me. It was in their interests for me to be great and good and they treated me that way no matter how I behaved. It's dangerous for a human to be celebrated without earning it. It makes you feel as though you're not responsible for your actions and can behave however you like. I was playing over three hundred shows a year. It was absolute madness and hugely exciting. I'd be in Portland, Oregon one day, then at the Byron Bay Bluesfest back in Australia the next, then back in Seattle a day later. I'd do anything to get to the gigs I wanted to play. It was all headed in the right direction and I wanted it so badly.

Then, I didn't know much about mental health. I still had that archaic idea that to mention your mental health somehow suggested you were mentally unstable, and I shied away from thinking or talking about it. But I was having huge ups and downs. Playing shows like that is an enormous high and an overwhelming social experience. Hundreds or even thousands of people wanting a little slice of you and wanting to tell you how much they love you and shower you with enthusiasm. I learnt how much I love to please people. I became addicted to it. I'd give everything I had on stage and come off a sweaty mess with a big smile. And then I would spend hours talking to every person afterwards and trying to match their enthusiasm and energy. I'd talk and hug and smile and laugh.

It was all positive and beautiful, but it was also socially exhausting. This was 'positive stress' and I was high on it. I'd finally get back to the band room and drink myself silly. I was young, I could bounce back. I'd start shovelling chips or sandwiches or beers or whiskey into my mouth or sucking back cigarettes or weed or whatever was around. Anything not to start coming down from that wild excited enthusiastic place the whole show experience had taken me to. It normally took getting high or drunk to finally fall asleep. I'd get a few hours, maybe five if I was lucky, and then it would be time to travel. Get lost. Be late. Miss flights. Everything that's in between the gigs. It was absolutely hectic. A fourteen-hour drive to the next show or a 4 am flight. Rental cars, visas and border crossings. Broken gear. Stolen gear. Lost gear. It all just rushes by you in a crazy blur. And things go wrong all the time so that suddenly, you're going to let down a room full of people. The cycle continued each day. Highly stressful travel and logistical pirouettes followed by giving every ounce of joy I had each evening.

I'd be in need of downtime but had no idea how to get it. If I even got close to taking time off I'd experience horrible comedowns. I'd feel like nowhere was home. Like a mouse stuck in a room with no mouse hole to run to. All the love and adoration would be gone and I'd have no idea how to regulate my emotions or create my own confidence. My love for myself was completely dependent on my gigs and the adoration of others. In retrospect, I had very low self-esteem. If I wasn't gigging myself half to death and having success in chasing down my dreams I'd feel small and like an imposter. You never catch fame. You never sit back in contentment. You're always chasing that next level and it's an addiction.

The hardest thing I've found in my journey is how to regulate emotionally. How not to get carried away by the highs of touring and playing music for people, and on the other side of the coin, how to remain joyful and self-assured when it's all gone away. After one of my first huge low experiences (which lasted about eighteen months), I started gratitude journalling. I'd write a little list each day of things I was grateful for and things I was hopeful for. At first, I'd be embarrassed to tell people. But over the last eight years I've found it's helped me through some of the darkest times of my life. I've learnt with gratitude journalling that the smaller the better. If I'm in a good headspace, I'll be grateful for the cup of tea I'm drinking or the smile I received from the guy at the petrol station, or the silence that held the gentle sound of the first birdsong on a morning hike. My 'hopeful-fors' include to laugh a lot, or to offer someone a space to talk about something troubling them, or to stumble across an old friend. Going into the micro grounds me in the present moment. I learn a lot from considering my entries each day. It's been a huge help. It also helps create habitual and subconscious gratitude. I catch myself feeling grateful for things without even consciously choosing to.

I also started meditating a few years ago and this has facilitated a huge transformation in my life. It helps me stay aware of those positive stress levels without getting caught up in a hyper mode where I can't relax. I notice if I march backstage looking for food or drink or weed. Now, instead of consuming whatever feels good to keep the high going, I sit with the reality of how I'm feeling. I let the overwhelming emotions rush over me and then start to fade. I no longer get scared when I feel them leaving. I know they'll be back tomorrow at the next show. It's rational and considered. I get to the hotel room and have a cup of tea and read a book and am calm enough for the sleep that my body and mind desperately need.

I meditate two or three times a day for ten to fifteen minutes. Sometimes it's really hard to make time. But I've learnt that the more resistance I have, the more attachment I have to emotional patterns that are overruling my present-moment awareness and clouding my clarity. These emotional patterns are often high states of anxiety and I need to witness them. They include the 'anything could go wrong at any moment' feelings from living on the road, and the post-show comedown fears. Meditating stops this emotional hijacking in its tracks.

I've also learnt that some form of exercise each day is hugely beneficial to me. It sends beautiful endorphins rushing through my body and leaves me with a sense of aliveness and strength. It reassures me that I have strength and that I can cope with difficulties. Throw in a cold shower afterwards and I really feel calm.

Between all these practices, a feeling of balance and centredness emerges. Whatever happens that day on the road, I'll be able to cope. Sooner or later, I'll be back in a hotel room with a cup of tea and a clear mind ready for bed. Things might have got crazy. The car might have broken down and a whole crazy series of events might have unfolded. But from within the whirlwind I am calm and rational. I believe in myself and love myself whether I go through the wild cycle of love and energy that a gig creates or whether I spend the day alone. I love myself for the calm person who exists in the middle of that tornado of joy and excitement and when it leaves I'm still standing there. And I'm still okay.

Overthinking?
Overwhelmed?
Stressed?

Take some time to
come back to your
breath and bring
yourself back to the
present moment.

Find a comfortable position with a straight spine.
Relax your shoulders. Unclench your jaw.
Loosen the muscles around your face.

Now, focus on your breath.
Pay attention to the rise and fall of your belly.

GENTLY INHALE THROUGH THE NOSE
SLOWLY EXHALE THROUGH THE MOUTH
LET IT GO

Continue breathing with awareness. Notice if your mind has wandered off. Be gentle with yourself and bring your attention back to your breath. Focus on the inhale. Focus on the exhale.

TAKE ANOTHER DEEP BREATH IN THROUGH THE NOSE
SLOWLY EXHALE THROUGH THE MOUTH
LET IT GO

Thoughts will come and go. Distractions may arise. This is normal and expected. Simply acknowledge them, let them pass and come back to your breath.

Don't forget that you have one of the most powerful tools already within you.

So when it all gets a little much, *just breathe.*

A GENTLE REMINDER
THAT IT IS OK...

to make mistakes

to have bad days

to focus on yourself

to break down

to rest and recover

to take time off

to be selfish

to reach out for help

IT IS OK TO NOT BE OK

'You never
know what's
behind a smile'

@sundaylemonade_

Loz Lemons

LOZ IS ONE HALF OF THE LIVELY MUSIC DUO SUNDAY LEMONADE, AND SPENDS HER DAYS TOURING AUSTRALIA WITH THE OTHER HALF, HER PARTNER TYSON, IN THEIR HOME ON WHEELS. WITH AN INFECTIOUS STAGE PRESENCE, LOZ SPREADS HER JOY TO OTHERS WHILE ALSO SHINING LIGHT ON THE REALITY OF MENTAL HEALTH.

I've never had an official mental health diagnosis but I've certainly been through plenty of battles. It's tricky to pinpoint when it all began but the most obvious starting point was when I was fifteen.

I have always been anxious but it really came to the surface when I started having physical health issues. All I wanted was to fit in and be 'normal', but I became uncomfortable when I was playing sport or generally being active, which I loved doing! I was diagnosed with a heart condition which led to three surgeries, several panic attacks in the middle of school and lots of ambulance trips to emergency. It felt like I had no control. I was also battling a severe phobia to needles.

After high school I had no real idea of who I was. I had confidence issues that became worse as I went through a full-time dance course, and endured an emotionally abusive and controlling relationship. I missed a lot of days of the course, got kicked out of final performance pieces and spent a lot of time at home in bed feeling very sorry for myself. As I moved towards the next chapter of my life at university, my clever dad subtly pointed me to a website he was using as a chatline relationship counsellor that he 'wanted my opinion on'. I read through the page where it listed signs of an unhealthy relationship. My heart broke as the dots connected and I realised that I was experiencing the majority of the points listed.

Years later, I found myself slowly slipping back into a black hole, drinking too much, failing my classes, feeling like I didn't belong, isolating myself and spending a lot of time crying into my pillow with the curtains closed. I'd been on the birth control pill for around six years and had so many complications, but doctors' recommendations never included learning how my body functioned but simply to try the next pill. None of them resulted in an easing of my symptoms. My beautiful mother noticed I was slipping and gently asked what was going on and brought up the birth control. I stopped taking it the next day. Within a week, the world began to look more colourful and I had a little sparkle back again.

The pandemic brought extra stress and anxiety into my life with the unknown, misinformation and fear. I was certain with my history of heart problems I'd soon be in hospital with an enlarged heart. At the same time, I was too scared to catch this earth-shaking virus without some sort of protection. Following my first vaccine I experienced an intensified heartbeat, shortness of breath and strange shooting pains all over my body but particularly in my chest, my hands and toes. After two weeks of battling I went to emergency where all tests returned normal results. Although I'll never know, I assume my symptoms were from anxiety.

Over the years, I've continued to have complications with my heart. The anxiety of my teens resurfaces with each trip back to emergency. In 2021, I was making dinner when my heart started racing out of my chest. This wasn't a total surprise as I have previously been diagnosed with a fast heartbeat, a slow heartbeat and my heart skips a beat frequently. But this particular occasion felt different. It was an hour before I made the call to head to the hospital.

I felt like I was in my teens again and had lost all control. Time and time again, I've been in emergency with tears streaming down my face as the medical staff roll their eyes at me because I wouldn't be showing any symptoms by the time they tended to me. I've had countless appointments where I've been told, 'This problem isn't going away,' or 'You'll end up with a pacemaker one day.' Without any clear answers, I've started seeing my heart and myself as a ticking time bomb. Each episode feels as though I'll implode, slowly losing the trust for my body to do what it has always done: live. When I feel a wave of anxiety, my body starts to buzz and my heart races, similar to how I experience tachycardia. It's a real battle to bring myself back to my body, to trust that it knows how to survive, and to settle my mind.

I was discharged after a few hours. It always spins me out that things can feel so dire in one moment then I'm sent home to go on living in another. I went into total shock for days, disconnected from myself and the world around me. The birds sounded weird, cars passing by became droning and distant, my hands and feet weren't mine. I couldn't eat, couldn't fathom doing anything but cry. It was a phone call to Beyond Blue and an understanding household that encouraged a shower, a silly TV show and rest that helped me get through.

Thankfully and despite all of this, I've found myself in a wonderful life. I'm a full-time musician in a happy, high-energy folky duo, 'Sunday Lemonade'. I've been almost constantly touring Australia for over three years in a campervan home with my partner, spreading joy wherever we can. The lifestyle is challenging, being on the road can be a rollercoaster, combined with an incredibly social job that puts me in front of people constantly. I am forever learning to navigate self-critical thoughts and worrying about other people's judgement while performing. It's an incredibly competitive industry even if it's unintentional! There are some days I get so wound up thinking I haven't got anything worth sharing and comparing myself to people more successful, more beautiful, more talented than me. But there should be room for all art, we need it!

I always find it interesting talking with friends who've seen me play a show. They never have any idea that beyond the big smile, the jigging and guitar swinging, inside my head a whole belittling, anxious conversation is playing out.

We can never really know what's going on for other people no matter how big their smile, how bubbly the conversation or how normal they may seem.

How did you keep swimming?

Having parents who support me and who work within mental health has been VERY handy. My mum studied to become a psychologist part time for fifteen years while I was growing up so she was always discussing things as she learnt them. I loved being involved in mock assessments around the dining table amongst the piles of notes and books. She thrived as a mature-aged student and through it taught me a lot about the mind, learned habits and perspectives. She recommended I see a psychologist to work through the needle phobia, which led to hypnotherapy, and coming out of that rough relationship. If you can go in with an open mind, the chance to sit down and gain an outside perspective might shake up the routine thoughts and start to pave new pathways.

Also, seeing and hearing those around me handle their own battles, unashamed of seeming weak and unafraid to be vulnerable, helps me—if they can make it through, I can too.

When the cloud starts to pass, I try to take time to be grateful for the little things like cute flowers, epic wildlife, strong, towering trees that outlast us, walking along the ocean picking up seashells. Mindfulness and presence are powerful tools to bring me back to my short existence here in the world.

What do you do when you notice your mental health declining?

I'm learning that usually it means I need to slow down and think about doing something for myself for a moment. Ideally, I'd like to say I move more slowly taking mindful walks, journalling, doing yoga, but the reality is I might do these things separately over a few days or weeks. I find it hard to create habits even when I know they're good for me!

In a more easy, practical sense, I've started taking more deep breaths and there's one process in particular I really love. Take a breath through your nose, then pause. Take another breath through your nose on top of that so you're super full all the way to the tip-top of your lungs, then let it all out your mouth with a little sigh if you're feeling it.

It washes away tension and I can think more clearly almost immediately!

I attempt to change up my self-talk by reminding myself that I am safe, I am loved, I am strong and I am healthy. Perhaps this is more relevant for me with my history of health conditions but the gentle reminders change my thoughts from self-destructive spirals and help me to feel calmer. They remind me those thoughts are temporary, but these statements are permanent.

I've also started reading fictional books again. I find it better for getting out of my head than a movie or TV show.

103

What advice would you give to someone struggling with their mental health?

It's a cliché and hard to do but talking always helps me. Often when I hear my whirling thoughts come out of my mouth, they feel absurd and far from the truth. Even if it's as simple as telling someone close to you that you're not doing great, you don't know what will help but you'd appreciate them checking in on you. My best friend and I do this for each other. We're pretty useless at keeping regular contact but when I'm feeling low I let her know. Seeing her name pop up and a simple, 'Thinking of you. How are you today?' makes me feel loved and important. If talking is intimidating, maybe writing would be better. Write without judgement, as if it will never be seen or read ever, by anyone.

I think it's hard in our modern world of constant stimulation and comparison not to let your mind win. Try to remember to be kind and patient with yourself. Take it one day at a time. Tomorrow is a chance to try again even if it's just a little change. Each day you get through is a big win!

"Sometimes when you're in a dark place you think you've been buried, but you've actually been planted"

—Christine Caine—

BECOME YOUR VERY BEST FRIEND

Would you speak to a friend the way you speak to yourself?

As humans, we pour our love into others, often without giving that same level of love to ourselves. We talk about ourselves so negatively, and that often becomes our version of the truth.

I have been guilty of speaking negatively to myself my entire life. 'I'm ugly. I'm not funny. I have no friends. I'm too weird. Nobody likes me. I'm not good enough. I'm annoying everybody. I'm so weak. I don't fit in anywhere. I hate myself.' These thoughts and more have run wild and uncontrollably through my mind. They became part of my daily narrative and over time, they were tearing me down.

I was feeling particularly vulnerable one morning during a session with my psychologist, and after seeing this, she simply asked what was going through my mind. One by one I started listing off all the negative thoughts I believed about myself after years of thinking them every single day.

Without any judgement, she simply asked, 'Would you talk to a friend the way you speak to yourself?'

The truth was, I could never imagine saying anything like that to someone. So why was it okay to talk to myself like that? Imagine the hurt and pain those words would inflict on a friend. And yet, I was inflicting that suffering on myself every single day. I needed to stop hurting myself with my own words. I needed to start treating myself like I was my best friend. I realised I'd been a bully to myself for far too long, and it was time to switch that narrative.

HOW TO KEEP SWIMMING

If you catch yourself focusing on those negative thoughts, take a moment to check in with yourself and ask yourself whether you would treat your friend the way you are treating yourself.

When I was caught in the whirlwind of my thoughts, and bullying myself, I found that by asking myself that question my thoughts would stop spiralling. From there, I could work on treating myself with kindness and compassion. I had to become my own best friend.

If you wouldn't speak to your friend a certain way, then give yourself that same respect. Become your very best friend. Speak to yourself the way you would speak to someone you love. Give yourself a hug from time to time. Embrace yourself with both arms and hold tight. Tell yourself that you are smart, caring, loving and kind. Tell yourself the things you love about yourself. Tell yourself that you are worthy. Learn to give yourself love the same way you love others. You will go through enough hardships in your life, so be careful not to add to them. You are the one constant in your life—give yourself love and you will flourish.

You are worthy.

there is a past

that is so proud

you've come

version of you

of how far

'A hug from a stranger
saved my life'

@gedm.oriarty

Ged Moriarty

GED IS A LOVER OF HUMANS, SPREADING JOY TO ANYONE HE MEETS. WITH AN IMMENSE GRATITUDE FOR LIFE, HE SPENDS HIS DAYS BEING UNAPOLOGETICALLY HIMSELF. AFTER FINDING THE LIGHT AFTER HIS DARKEST DAYS, GED USES HIS VOICE TO RAISE AWARENESS FOR MENTAL HEALTH AND IS A PASSIONATE ACTIVIST FOR FEMINISM.

My struggle with mental health started when I was seven or eight. I remember wanting to stab myself with a knife. I used to think this was a product of being young and naive, but it was the beginning of my depression.

Growing up was tough, as my father was often emotionally abusive, and occcassionally physically. However, my biggest struggle with depression was between 2018 and 2021. In January 2018, my parents (thankfully) split after a violent episode involving my father. It was tough having two homes, especially because all I wanted was to be with my mom. This period coincided with breaking up with my girlfriend of four years, one of the most wonderful people I know. I told her that I didn't want to bring her down, and though she fought for me, our relationship ended. This further isolated me from the world as she was my number one support person.

I never got time to sit with these emotions, as I moved to on-campus accommodation for university in February 2018. While I will be forever grateful for the memories and friends made there, campuses have a massive drug and alcohol culture which I fell victim to. In my first week at college, I was raped by a girl who lived at my sister college. The toxic masculinity within me and my friends was very evident after this occasion. 'At least you got laid,' my friends would say. Little did I know she had reported that I had raped her, and I was forced to apologise to a number of people. It wasn't until she let slip that her accusations were not true, and that I was actually the victim, that people began to believe my side of the story. Consequently, I received an apology from members of her college but no action was taken against her, and I had to see her nearly every week for my three-year stint on campus.

In March 2018, I jumped into a new relationship with a girl who was extremely physically abusive, and I put up with her behaviour until January 2019. A few months later, I entered a new relationship with a girl who was very manipulative and emotionally abusive. She cheated on me multiple times and had excuses that made me feel terrible. 'You weren't giving me the love I deserve so I went elsewhere'; 'I told you that we had slept together (she didn't) so why are you all of a sudden mad about this now?'

In November 2019, she broke up with me. In February 2020, this same woman told me that she was sixteen weeks pregnant with my child. This completely ruined me, but I needed to take responsibility for my actions. However, she enlightened me later that month that the baby was not real by saying, 'I just did a pregnancy test and it's negative, I only thought I was pregnant because of my symptoms.'

I had a pretty heavy week on drugs and alcohol after that, and bumped into her on a night out on Valentine's Day. She asked to talk to me but I refused, saying neither of us was in the best state to do so. She reacted by throwing a glass at the back of my head.

After everything that had occurred over the previous two years, I thought, 'I just don't want to be alive anymore.'

I walked to the nearest train station and found the platform of the next incoming train. I stood there, waiting for the train due in two minutes, completely content with throwing myself in front of it. My thoughts were foggy and I was crying, but in that moment it seemed the only option.

Then, a complete stranger hugged me from behind and sat me down on the ground. They hugged me until the train flew past, and I was crying so violently I couldn't think. I didn't even realise that the person had left, and I was left sitting alone on the platform. I don't remember how I got home that night, but I had to get my act together because orientation week was beginning at 8 the following morning, and I was on the team to welcome new residents to the college.

I started seeing a psychologist throughout 2020. This was mainly focused on dealing with my father and we never got into the depths of my struggles with depression. I never told anyone about that night at the train station until I opened up to a new girlfriend in November 2020. Even though I had got through that experience, I was still feeling that I was distracting myself and wasn't truly happy. I broke up with that girlfriend in October 2021 because I wasn't happy with my life. It was a tough break-up, but it also felt like the first step in prioritising my own feelings regardless of how it looked from the outside.

Heading into 2022, I decided to make my New Year's resolution 'take responsibility for my own happiness', and I did. Every single day, I now do things I love and I don't care what other people think of me. If it makes me happy, I am going to do it. I have started taking antidepressants every day because they work! The biggest reason for improvement, however, was admitting my trauma to myself, and not being ashamed to talk about it to other people. True happiness doesn't just appear and stay forever, it's something we need to work on every day. I have troughs and highs, but I know there is so much beauty in the world. I also know I am in a significantly better place now than I was in the previous four years. I'm proud of myself for that.

How did you keep swimming?

From the moment I tried to take my own life, I have done two main things to keep swimming: small acts of kindness and hugging EVERYONE!

I find exquisite joy in seeing other people joyful! I always have, and getting through 2020 and 2021, I used small acts of kindness and gift-giving to help myself get through the toughest of times. I learnt a Pali word, 'mudita', which translates to 'the joy of seeing other people's joy'. When you break down every action of your daily life, you realise that giving people joy is easy. For example, in 2020 I started fist-pounding everyone—cashiers, waiters, my friends (every single day)! Often, I got left hanging because they didn't see or expect it—awkward—but when it was reciprocated, it always brought on a face-splitting smile. I often allowed cars to cut in front of me, or opened doors for strangers. I would go out of my way to compliment people, and always say please and thank you and mean it! The best times were doing something for someone when they didn't know it was me, like buying a stranger their coffee or doing my housemate's chores for the week. That's one way I kept swimming, because those simple and easy moments of joy fuelled me with so much light and beauty! I must note that I also did joyful things for myself, and thanked myself aloud! I'd buy a new plant and tell myself, 'Thank you for this gift,' or I would skip a gym day and thank myself for listening to my body. Seeing joy in myself was beautiful, and thanking myself for the moment allowed me to embody that feeling!

My second tactic is to hug everyone and hug with purpose! A hug from a stranger literally saved my life and I will never be able to thank that person, but I will never take for granted this form of affection ever again. When I need a mood boost, I ask my friends for a hug (or not ask, just do it and they always reciprocate). Every time I see a friend I haven't seen for a long time, I hug them, not just once but multiple times while we're together. I hug waitstaff and cashiers if I feel like it, and it's funny because no one has ever said no. As human beings, we all crave affection. Hugging strangers not only helps me keep swimming, but also gives them the love and affection they need and crave. Obviously if someone said no, I would respect their wishes. Hug the people around you, and hug them often— you never know when it will be your last!

What do you do when you notice your mental health declining?

I fall back on doing things I love the most without guilt, even if this means cancelling plans. I love playing my guitar, reading my book, taking coffee to the park and people-watching, going to the beach and watching sunsets. I am very lucky to have a workplace that is accepting of mental health days, and friends who understand that I will continue to prioritise myself above anything else. I am very appreciative that my friends allow me to be vulnerable so I do not need to hide my emotions. I will message them and say, 'Hi, I just need time to myself because I'm not feeling great, let's reschedule our plans!' I do not apologise, because I have learnt that I never owe people anything, and I will never be sorry for putting myself first.

I drop all electronics and sit with myself, so I can be present. Rather than trying to understand the feeling, or assign it to something, I just let the feelings of sadness/anxiety flow through me like the energy they are. Doing the things I love gives me hope that there is beauty in the world, and while I am struggling to see it now, the smallest of things can show me. I know the low energy will soon pass. I don't need to force it, just help it by falling back on the things I love to do. It is different for everyone, so find yours! Notice the times when you are happy, jot them down and do them when you are struggling.

What advice would you give to someone struggling with their mental health?

My biggest piece of advice for people struggling with mental health is to give yourself some CREDIT! We often assign hero-like behaviour to sporting stars and musicians, and while they may do admirable things, I believe the real MVPs in the world are those struggling with their mental health. These individuals do not get enough credit for the effort they put into daily life. Suicide often passes through people's minds, yet no one gives people with suicidal thoughts the credit they deserve for conquering those thoughts and continuing every single day. People with eating disorders don't get the credit they deserve for fighting the urge to resist it. People who can't get out of bed still do it every day, despite what their mind is telling them. These people are fucking phenomenal humans, and deserve to be acknowledged. It's so easy for mental illnesses to destroy a person, but people who don't allow this to happen (even though it might not feel this way) are really my heroes.

My second piece of advice for depression and/or anxiety is not to be afraid to take antidepressants! There is such a stigma against them and it is silly. I was a victim to the mindset 'I don't want to label myself as depressed and I will be if I am on drugs' until the day I was told that these little pills aren't the source of my happiness, they are just a gatekeeper. I do not feel instantly happy when I take my antidepressants. They help the 'happiness' chemicals in my body work, as this aspect of my body is flawed for some reason. It is still my job to make myself happy. I still have bad days on the pills, and that's because they are not magical sources of joy.

You need to do the work yourself. If you know you would be happier if you meditated for five minutes every day, or journaled every night, then you would do it. It's all about acting, taking that extra step, as inaction gets you nowhere.

Learn to put your needs first.

Think about when your plane is about to depart, and the aircrew start running through the emergency procedures. They always say to put your oxygen mask on first before helping others with theirs. This is such a great example of a truth we need to acknowledge more: 'If you don't help yourself first, you won't be in a position to help anyone else.'

With that in mind, please know that it is okay to:

REST WHEN YOU NEED TO TO REST
STOP WHEN YOU NEED TO STOP
SAY NO WHEN YOU DON'T WANT TO SAY YES
DO WHAT FEELS RIGHT FOR YOU WHEN OTHERS MAY NOT AGREE
SEEK HELP WHEN YOU ARE STRUGGLING

It is okay to make yourself a priority, to take care of yourself and to focus on yourself. In fact, it is necessary. Put yourself first and the rest will follow.

DON'T FORGET THAT
YOU HAVE SURVIVED 100%
OF YOUR WORST DAYS
YOU CAN GET THROUGH
ANYTHING

STRUGGGLES WITH IDENTITY

One of the biggest contributors to the decline of my mental health was my loss of identity/sense of self. I spent the first six years of my twenties in the navy, where my identity was handed to me. I was given values and purpose and told how to act and who I needed to be. My first name, the name I had attached every inch of myself to for my entire life, was no longer to be used. I was to be addressed by my rank, followed by my last name. I became known just by my surname, 'Easlea'. Who I was before joining was slowly broken down, and bit by bit, I became a creation of the Defence Force.

It came as no surprise that when I left the navy in 2019, I began to struggle every single day, desperately searching for the answer to the question, 'Who am I?' I had to rediscover who Annaleise Easlea was outside of Defence. What were my values? What was my purpose? The answers to those questions were given to me at the very start of my Defence career. When I was serving, I used to be able to introduce myself and say, 'I'm in the navy,' and with those four words, people would know more about me than I could have ever told them. Once I was out of Defence, I felt that my introductions ran short. I didn't have anything to say about myself as I did not even know who I was. My name quickly became the only thing about myself that I knew was certain.

Trying to figure out who I was meant to be and what my purpose in life was became incredibly overwhelming. I felt as though everything I knew had been stripped from me once again, the same way it was on the day I enlisted in the navy. I was left trying to put together the pieces of a puzzle when I had no idea what the finished product was meant to look like. I needed to rediscover who I was without Defence forming part of my identity. To help with this mind-boggling puzzle, my psychologist and I ran through an exercise that turned out to be more powerful than I realised at the time.

I was asked to imagine that I was introducing myself to a room full of people during an icebreaker activity. **What would my dream introduction be?** Would I feel excited about what I was saying? Who would I like to be known as? Would I be proud of my introduction? After giving it some thought, I created my dream introduction. While this introduction may not have been my reality at that moment, it gave me the hope that I needed to take the steps towards forming my dream identity.

I wrote down my dream introduction. 'My name is Annaleise. I am a happily married solo traveller. I'm an author and am learning the Spanish language. I'm a survivor of mental illness.' In just a few short sentences, I knew who Annaleise Easlea could become and this gave me something to work towards.

I was then able to look at my life and identify what I needed to change to get one step closer to achieving this dream introduction and forming this identity. When I started to do this, I realised something wasn't sitting well with me about the introduction I had written. So I gave myself permission to look inwards and ask the tough questions. Was this aspect of my life bringing me joy, or was I conforming to this identity because of societal pressures or others' expectations? By asking these tough questions, I was able to really assess if something was serving me. It was then that I listened to my gut and recognised that being married was not something I felt aligned with. As much as I tried, I knew deep down that it was not bringing me joy, and so I made the tough decision to leave.

The beauty of identity is that it is ever-changing. Now if I was asked what my dream introduction is, I would say, 'My name is Annaleise. I am a solo traveller. I'm an author and am passionate about advocating for mental health.

I am on a never-ending journey to keep my inner peace.'

Piece by piece, I am putting together the puzzle that is Annaleise Easlea, and I can finally see what it might look like.

HOW TO KEEP SWIMMING

If you're struggling with the question of 'Who am I?' then consider what you would like to say in an icebreaker if you were asked to introduce yourself. What is your dream introduction? By answering this, you have a dream identity that you can work towards.

131

Give yourself permission to ask the tough questions:

IS THIS SERVING ME?

IS THIS BRINGING ME JOY?

IS THIS FOR ME OR IS THIS FOR OTHERS?

DO I WANT THIS OR AM I FOLLOWING THIS PATH BECAUSE SOCIETY SAYS TO?

Then, bit by bit, you can identify if there are changes you need to make in your path so you can walk towards something that resonates with you more.

go slow   it takes
time to grow

'A misdiagnosis
changed my path'
@shayellelajoie

Shayelle Lajoie

SHAYELLE IS A PASSIONATE BIOMEDICAL STUDENT AND YOGA INSTRUCTOR. COMBINING HER LOVE FOR AND KNOWLEDGE OF HEALTH AND FITNESS, SHAYELLE NOW RUNS RETREATS TO SHARE WITH OTHERS THE POSITIVE IMPACT THAT NUTRITION, MINDFULNESS AND MOVEMENT CAN HAVE ON OUR LIVES.

When I was twenty-four, I was misdiagnosed with bipolar by a psychologist I was seeing at the time on the free Medicare rebate system. They did not tell me where to go from there or what to do about it. It sounds crazy that a misdiagnosis like that can happen.

I felt as though it could have been related to my nutrition. At the time, I was eating a super-high-sugar diet, snacking on chocolate and lollies all day. Naturally, this would cause me to have ups and downs and change my personality to an extent.

It was an incredibly sloppy admin screw-up on their part, and not following it up really damaged me over the next few years. I believed that I wasn't worthy of people's attention as I was worried that I was either in a manic high or on a super-depressive low. I thought it was unfair on other people for me to be myself as I believed I would drain others because of my apparent personality disorder.

Although it turned out to be a huge misunderstanding, it was all I had been told so it became all I knew.

Since then, I have spent many years studying nutrition on my own. After reading so many books on the topic by experts in their field, I became super-passionate about it and was able to apply what I learnt to myself. This truly allowed me to grow and learn. I started listening to *The Proof* podcast, which was a big learning curve. I began noticing the effect on my body of eating wholefoods and moving away from refined sugar. I felt like a different person. I began thinking clearly and could feel my feelings properly, rather than riding highs and lows. When I was twenty-nine, I signed up for a science pathway course for university. Until then, I did not believe I was academic or worthy enough and because of my high-sugar diet, my thoughts were scattered and I could never focus for more than a few minutes at a time.

Surprising myself, I scored ninety-nine, ninety-eight and ninety-seven in chemistry, biology and statistics. Now I am in my third year of Biomed at USC and loving it. My life is completely different from how it used to be.

I now prioritise yoga. I prioritise my mental health. I prioritise my off days and I prioritise my boundaries. I make sure I take the time to settle after busy days, weeks or months. I prioritise healthy relationships. I'm really happy that I'm now in this place.

When I was thirty-one, I appeared on the show *Survivor* and we had a psychologist working with us throughout the show. Then, outside of the game, he took me through the whole protocol of how one should be diagnosed with bipolar and I didn't even come close to meeting the minimum requirements. After years of believing I had bipolar, he officially confirmed that it was a misdiagnosis and I felt so much weight come off my shoulders.

Survivor taught me how to have strong mental health. I was able to get through being on the bottom, being excluded, being bullied, having people roll their eyes at me, snicker at me as I walked past, shrug and screw up their faces when I won. It hurt at the time and it hurts to watch the reruns, but it all helped me grow, build resilience and build my mental and physical strength. I was able to stay in the game right until the end and not break under the pressure.

I now feel I'm in a really strong place. Even the psych at *Survivor* kept applauding my ability to tune out what others were saying and go into my meditative state. I don't believe that meditation should be used to ignore or suppress those things but to help you move towards a headspace of gratitude. Simply taking yourself out of drama and negative thinking and turning it into gratitude is a huge superpower.

How did you keep swimming?

131

Definitely my meditative practice. Also, and this may sound corny but it is true, my pure joy for life. I feel like I spend every second day on social media saying, 'Just stop with the negative thoughts. Look around you and find the joy in life.' As I say that, I am looking up and watching the leaves flow in the wind, the colours of the sunset changing, the clouds scudding by and thinking how freaking lucky we are to be on this earth. Why not enjoy it and soak it all up, make friends and feel and flow with love?

Time. Make time for yourself. I noticed that I was saying, 'Yes, yes, yes,' to all these things. Yet I would end up disappointing myself and feeling terrible that I couldn't turn up to all the events I committed to. However, the moment I sit down and put pen to paper I can prioritise things and work out what I need to do for myself. After this, I instantly have a clear head.

Most of the time when I feel a deep, dark time arising, I need to just say no and prioritise myself. I'll say no to commitments, take a slow morning walk, cook a wholesome meal, swim, surf and just meditate.

What do you do when you notice your mental health declining?

Anxiety comes up in my everyday life, sometimes daily. When I was in my mid to late twenties, there were some days when I couldn't leave the house. I'd worry that if I ran down to the surf with my surfboard, the surf wouldn't be any good and I'd have to walk back, dry and embarrassed that I hadn't got into the water. Then I would say to myself, I'll go for a jog instead. I'd put my joggers on, get ready and then worry that I'd bump into my ex or run past my workplace and they'd ask me to work. Any random situation would come into my head and freak me out. All those possibilities, even if they were unlikely, seemed inevitable. I'd put on some comfortable clothes and walk to the farmers market but I couldn't make a single decision. I can see now that this mental chatter was far-fetched yet I believed it at the time. I would stay indoors all day and by 2 in the afternoon I would be angry that I had wasted an entire day, and this would build upon the next day's anxiety.

To address it, I say aloud, 'I'm feeling anxious today. I don't know why. It's bugging me, but I will get to the bottom of it and even if I don't it will be okay. Today is another day.' I will then make myself list three things that I'm grateful for (if there's someone in my house, I'll whisper it) but usually I try and say it in an affirming way like, 'Far out, the sky is so beautiful. There is a nice light breeze and I cannot wait to feel the sun on my face outside.' After this, I will feel a slight shift in my mindset and even though it doesn't completely take me out of my anxiety, it helps me to remember how grateful I am just to be alive.

There is also journalling, taking time to put pen to paper and writing down my feelings. Sometimes I'll do a mind map and try to find where a feeling or thought has come from. I'll write down my anger, frustration, disappointment, anxiety, dizziness or confusion and link these words with feelings like 'let down by boyfriend', 'disappointed by friend', 'insecure about this', 'unsure about those plans'. If it's something specific, I try to break it down further: 'that thing she did last week', or 'what he said in the text yesterday'. Once it is down on paper, I feel like it's out there and there's nothing to be afraid of or worried about.

One of the greatest ways to relieve anxious feelings is to take a walk or get out in nature. You can't help but smile and feel a connection to Earth. You notice cute things: a family next to you walking, surfers running down to the beach. There is so much life outside and it is not to be missed. Whenever I've said I'll just have a quick three- to four-minute walk around the block, I'll always end up jogging up the street, bumping into the neighbours, having a chat then doing a two-kilometre run. I'll then walk back and stop halfway at the park to meditate. It ALWAYS ends up being better than I expect.

The same goes with yoga. I often think I'll just do a couple of downward dog poses and child's pose for two minutes and the next thing I know, it's been an hour and a half. I'll have piano music playing, incense lit, lights dimmed and I'm just oozing happiness and joy out of my flow. My breath slows down, my blood pressure decreases and it is just beautiful.

141

Some days, when so many things seem to go wrong and my mind won't stop attaching to the disappointment or sadness, a jog and a journal don't quite cut it. After a long day at university, an argument with a loved one or simply going shopping and something triggers me, I get in my car, have a quick cry and then call my best friend to talk about how ridiculous it is. We laugh it off and it truly feels like medicine. Or I play calm classical music and take slow deep breaths so my thoughts slow down and take up less space in my mind.

What advice would you give to someone struggling with their mental health?

Firstly, I suggest taking a huge breath in. Literally, right now. Then, let it all go when you breathe out. Picture yourself bundling up all your shitty thoughts when you breathe in, shoving them into a massive santa sack, and as you breathe out, booting them off the edge of a cliff into the sea, never to be seen again. Do this whenever those thoughts come back.

Studying the power of the breath is huge for anyone struggling with their mental health. Before I learnt about breathwork I didn't get much out of my yoga classes. Going deeply into pranayama (the regulation of breath) is life-changing. It really is. It got me through the endurance challenges on Survivor and my social struggles.

Lastly, see a therapist. Even if you think you're on top of your mental health, it is still important to see a therapist, chat it out, nut it out. Sometimes we don't understand what our thoughts are doing or what we are triggered by. Having a conversation with someone who has trained for years to understand the complex mind is powerful.

My past self was always so busy, bound up and wound up with so much anxiety that I would cover up by drinking and taking drugs, getting involved in unhealthy pastimes at ungodly hours. If I could give one piece of advice to that younger girl it would be to 'press pause' and check in on yourself. Take a yoga class. Go for a walk and see where it takes you. Maybe you'll get a juice. Maybe you'll pick some flowers in a field and sit there listening to your own thoughts. Anything is possible when you finally press pause.

WHAT AM I GRATEFUL FOR TODAY?

FINDING THE STRENGTH
TO FOLLOW MY HEART

THE POWER OF CONNECTION
AND CONVERSATION

THE KINDNESS OF OTHERS WHEN
THEY SO EASILY GIVE WITHOUT
EXPECTING ANYTHING IN RETURN

LEARNING TO BE COMFORTABLE
IN MY OWN COMPANY

If you had asked me this question a couple of years ago, I would not have been able to answer it at all. When I was falling further into depression, I turned to gratitude journals to try and 'get better', but I would end up feeling worse. At the time, I had a roof over my head, a loving husband, supportive family and friends, a stable job, and yet I felt nothing at all. It was a deep struggle to say I was grateful for something and actually mean it.

Since then, there have been times when I have been able to feel gratitude intensely, which has helped me realise the power of gratitude. It helps us recognise and learn to appreciate the positive things in our life rather than focusing on the negative.

However, I still go through stages where I don't feel grateful for anything. Where my depressive episodes take over and cover my eyes so I can't see clearly. It is okay to go through periods like this.

Go easy on yourself. If you are struggling to find gratitude, take the pressure off yourself to feel it. I understand how hard it is to feel grateful when every day becomes a struggle.

Focus on what can help you to keep going. Take small steps. Just put one foot in front of the other. Work on what you can do to keep swimming.

Eventually, when your pain eases and your world starts to fill with colour again, gratitude might seep back into your life without you even realising it.

And like an old slab of concrete,
Flowers grew within her cracks.
Her most vulnerable places,
Bloomed with new growth.
And something that was once broken,
Became beautiful again.

LAURY HOUGHTON

'You are
not alone'

@thebarefoot_dutchman

Anton Nootenboom

ANTON IS A DUTCH ARMY VETERAN, HAVING SPENT TEN
YEARS IN THE SERVICE. HE WAS THE FIRST PERSON TO
CLIMB TO BASE CAMP MT EVEREST BAREFOOT AND WENT
ON TO RAISE AWARENESS FOR MEN'S MENTAL HEALTH BY
WALKING 3,019 KM BAREFOOT FROM CAIRNS TO SYDNEY.
NOW EVERY STEP ANTON MAKES IS TO HELP BREAK DOWN
THE STIGMA OF MENTAL HEALTH.

I served in the Dutch army for ten years including three tours to Afghanistan. My first realisation of what mental health means was when I returned from these missions. I slowly started noticing behavioural changes in my mates. Some friends would be more on edge, where background noises like a door slamming shut would trigger them. Some would be more agitated or aggressive, leading to more fights on and off the army bases. Relationships would end because girlfriends or wives weren't able to cope with the different husband or boyfriend who came back from Afghanistan. We never talked about it. You get to endure stress levels that most will never have to endure in a lifetime, yet you don't talk about it. You get to see and do things that most people will never have to see or do in their lives, yet you still don't talk about it.

I believe I am a lucky man. My mates and I walked out alive, and my brain is wired in a way that I was able to process everything myself. I would be on edge for a little while after a mission but then it would fade. I have managed to take the positive out of the negative and become aware of how lucky we are to be born and raised in a safe country like the Netherlands or Australia. I am aware of the fact that life can be over in a second, so live it like there is no tomorrow.

My own mental health chapter didn't start until much later. After I left the Dutch army, I moved to this paradise called Australia. For about two years, I was distracted by its beauty and all the fun and freedom of travelling, but as I started to settle, everything appeared on my plate at once. A very painful breakup was the start of Pandora's box opening. The breakup made me realise where I was standing in life and what I was lacking. I had sold my house in the Netherlands and was left with a massive debt that I didn't want to think about until there was no more hiding from it. Along with the financial pressure came a job that I absolutely hated at the time. I felt stuck in the situation but because I was on a student visa in Australia, I had no other option.

The biggest impact was the realisation that I had lost my identity. I did not know until then that when I left the army, I lost my sense of who I was. For ten years I was a soldier. That's how everyone knew me and that's how I knew myself. I had a goal- and purpose-driven life. Now I was no one. I had no direction in life, and no purpose. I was just floating around Australia. Heartbroken, with financial pressure, stuck in a job I hated, and no identity.

I started to get anxiety and panic attacks on jobs sites, and I could not bear showing up to work every day. So, I missed out on more money, which led to having to leave my room in a shared house and move to a six-bed dorm hostel. Sharing my room with a bunch of eighteen-year-olds that were absolutely frothing on life was not the best place for a thirty-one-year-old who was sliding into a deep depression. On job sites and in the hostel, the walls started to close in on me. I was a dark cloud that my friends didn't want to be around anymore, and I didn't want to be around them anymore. I felt like I was a burden. Even when I was with them, I felt lonely. So, I started to distance myself from them. Everything combined got me into a deep dark rabbit hole where all I had left to do, was talk to myself. And we are all our own worst critics. The more I talked to myself, the more I started to believe that I was a failure. A loser, a nobody.

How did you keep swimming?

I would leave the job sites and the hostel and walk. I would aimlessly pace up and down the Manly promenade. From Queenscliff to Shelly Beach, a stretch of 2.5 km, walking it for seven to nine hours a day, just so I was outside and didn't have to sit still with my own thoughts. I did this for weeks, maybe even months on end, without changing anything. I would see the ocean but feel nothing. I would see a sunrise but feel empty. Normally I would be so stoked and tell other people to look at how beautiful it was. Now I was numb.

One day, on one of these walks, I stopped, stood still and told myself, 'You can walk however much you want, but it will not change anything about your situation. If you want something to change, you need to do something different, and there is only one person that can do that and that's you.'

153

I had one very good friend left. Even though I drove her nuts sometimes with my negativity, she was always there for me. She was seeing a spiritual/mental health coach and invited me to go and see her. I had nothing to do with spirituality, but I had nothing to lose so decided to go. That was where my healing journey started. Talking to a professional was the change I needed. She gave me a book, *Mindfulness: Finding Peace in a Frantic World*. She also suggested an app called Headspace. The combination of these two things, mindfulness and meditation, were the tools I needed to feel more in control of my thoughts. I started to read more books about it, listen to podcasts and watch YouTube videos. Most importantly, I started to talk. The more I talked, the more I learnt it was perfectly fine to deal with my mental health and that many more people are dealing with it. I learnt the tools needed to become more resilient but I also became aware that experiencing emotions and showing them is fine. It took me two years of everyday work, with lots of ups and downs. But I came out stronger than ever before. I learnt more about myself in those two years than in the thirty-one years before.

What do you do when you notice your mental health declining?

I start with not judging it as bad or wrong. I just accept it as it is. Sometimes you feel good, sometimes you feel bad. It's perfectly fine. If you have a crap day, just have a crap day. You don't always have to feel good, that's toxic positivity. I determine if it's something I can control or not. If it's out of my control, I try to let it go. There is no point in worrying about something I cannot change. If it's something that's within my control, I check what I can do to change the situation. I think in solutions. It's not always easy, but it is always possible.

Usually when my mind goes a hundred miles an hour, my breathing is fast and shallow. The one thing you are always in control of is your breath. When you slow down your breath, you slow down your heartrate and have more space for clear thinking. I try not to focus too much on the past and future but stay in the present. What can I focus on right now? It can be the simplest thing like people passing by, or the leaves of a tree rustling in the wind. I give myself time to just be. I don't put pressure on myself to have to feel or be a certain way. Sometimes I feel better when by myself, and sometimes I think it's better to mingle and meet up with friends. I meditate. I take cold showers. I exercise. I go for nature walks. Things that stimulate the creation of endorphins and serotonin in my body, the happy and reward chemicals. But most of all, I am kind to myself. I talk to myself as I would talk to my best mate.

What advice would you give to someone struggling with their mental health?

Be kind to yourself. It is easy to get stuck in negative self-talk. Be open to conversations with friends or family that could change your perspective on things and lead to better solutions as to why you might be struggling with your mental health. Take it day by day, small steps at a time. Don't overwhelm yourself. Make small achievable goals to overcome your hurdles. You are not alone. Even though it can feel lonely at times, know there is always someone to talk to. You don't have to fight this battle alone. Know that you have everything it takes to overcome the inevitable curveballs life can throw at you. You don't have to know the answers to it all. You, like everyone else, are doing this thing called life for the first time. No one has all the answers. It's a learning process. It is perfectly fine to ask for a helping hand when you are in need.

155

Surfing came into my life at a time when I needed it most.
I needed something to help me escape the madness in
my mind.

When I'm sitting on my board in between sets, there is
nothing on my mind except for the present moment. I am
not thinking about my past. I am not worrying about my
future. I am just being.

The present moment exists outside of the ocean too.
If I am struggling to get out of my own head, I take myself
on a mindful walk. As I'm walking, I take time to think
about what I see, what I smell, what I hear and what I feel.
Focusing on this brings me back to the present moment,
giving my mind a rest from whatever was consuming it.

If your mind is working overtime today, take yourself outside. Go for a walk or find somewhere to sit.

Take some time to ask yourself:

WHAT CAN YOU SEE?
WHAT CAN YOU SMELL?
WHAT CAN YOU HEAR?
WHAT CAN YOU FEEL?

Give yourself a break from the worries of the past or the stresses of the future.

Try and enjoy the space between where you have been and where you are going.

It is NOW, and it can be pretty magical when you take the time to see it.

OUR EXPECTATIONS

Expectation can be defined as believing that something is going to happen or that something should be a certain way. Every day we place many expectations on ourselves, others, our feelings, our actions and our entire life. We often have a particular way or direction that we want things to go, and when it doesn't quite turn out as hoped, it can lead to feelings of disappointment and dismay.

Learning to manage my expectations has had an enormous impact on my journey. The importance of releasing expectations really hit home when I took a trip to Sri Lanka. In hindsight, I had nothing but the highest expectations of how I believed the trip would play out. I believed I would immediately feel at peace, go surfing every day, explore non-stop and not experience any discomfort whatsoever. I slowly came to learn that this expectation was unrealistic, and I had no control over what would happen next.

Two days into my trip, I took myself to a nearby café to work on this very book and have breakfast. It was 9 am. The café was well within walking distance, and it was broad daylight. As I walked to the café, I was so excited because everything was turning out just as I had hoped. Until it wasn't. I hadn't realised that a man had followed me down the street on his bike until I felt him grope me from behind. I immediately felt sick. I yelled at him, but he simply turned around and rode away, completely unphased by what he had just done. I was shaking as I walked towards the café. The rest of the morning was spent wiping my tears as I ate my turmeric oats. The experience had completely and utterly rocked me.

161

I began feeling scared and frightened to walk anywhere, especially alone. I rarely left the house on the days following as I was worried sick about being targeted again. I hated feeling vulnerable and unsafe. I even started to doubt coming to Sri Lanka and was racking my brain trying to figure out what I should do next. What am I doing here? Where's the safest place for a solo female traveller? Am I cut out for this? Should I just go home? This wasn't at all what I had expected, and strong feelings of disappointment started to creep in.

I reached a point where I had to find a way to move forward or leave Sri Lanka. After some reflecting, I could see that my expectations were the biggest cause of my disappointment. It was then that I sat with my feelings, practised letting go of my expectations and turned my focus towards the only thing that I could control—me. Even though the trip may not have started as I had hoped, it had the potential to be even better. By bringing awareness back to what I could control, I shifted my perspective and saw what had happened as a lesson, not a setback.

Once I let go of any expectations that I had for the trip, I was able to feel truly at peace. Anything became possible as it was no longer confined to what I thought should happen, and I went on to have a far better time than I ever could have imagined.

I then began to practise letting go of expectations daily. When disappointment arises, I question my expectations surrounding the situation. Am I being realistic? Is this something I have control over? More often than not, the answer is no and then I let go of those expectations.

For me, a life with no or minimal expectations became a life of freedom. My motto soon became, 'No expectations, no disappointment,' and this is something I now actively remind myself of every day. Each time I detach myself from the idea that something should pan out a particular way, I feel more at peace and can take comfort in knowing that anything truly is possible.

In this rollercoaster ride that we call life, nothing is guaranteed to turn out the way we wish. We must remind ourselves that some things are simply out of our control. Rather than dwelling on the unpleasant feelings that come along when our expectations aren't met, we need to practise shifting our energy inwards and start paying attention to what we can control—ourselves. By focusing on our thoughts, feelings and actions, we can choose how we react to a situation when it doesn't turn out as we expected.

HOW TO KEEP SWIMMING

If you are currently struggling, it's worthwhile taking a step back, reflecting on what is happening and determining if it is your unmet expectations that are causing you pain. Ask yourself if this expectation is realistic. Is this something in your control? By asking yourself these questions, you are bringing awareness to the fact that some things are beyond your control, and that is okay.

163

Start to focus on what you can control. Focus on your thoughts, feelings and actions. You can choose how you act in every situation, and similarly, you can choose how you see things. It doesn't have to be disappointing when things don't work out how you wanted, but rather, it can be a lesson. What is it teaching you?

If you can detach yourself from the belief that something should be a particular way, then you really open yourself up to far more possibilities and opportunities. It could turn out even better than you ever could have hoped for.

Remember, you always have the chance to look at, reflect on and question your expectations. You can shift your focus towards what you can control and choose your next steps. You have the power to change your perspective.

Don't let yourself be weighed down by something out of your control.

"IF IT COSTS YOU YOUR PEACE
IT'S TOO EXPENSIVE"

-PAULO COELHO-

'Post-natal depression
stole a year of my life'
@lifewith_courtney_

Courtney Welsh

COURTNEY IS A PROUD MUM OF TWO BOYS. AFTER BEING
BLESSED WITH A CHILD WITH A NEURODIVERGENCE AND
FACING HER OWN STRUGGLES WITH ANXIETY, COURTNEY
IS USING HER EXPERIENCE TO HELP OTHER PARENTS
FEEL SEEN AND LESS ALONE IN THEIR JOURNEY, NO MATTER
WHAT STAGE THEY ARE IN.

167

I strongly believe I have suffered from anxiety since I was a child. I look back now and after many years of therapy, education and greater awareness, I can see so many aspects of my life that were touched by the effects of anxiety. I just didn't know how bad it was going to get.

I was twenty-three years old when I gave birth to my first son. It was an incredibly traumatic birth. Somehow, I thrived through the shift into motherhood. It was incredible. I was a calm and loving mother. My husband worked a lot, so it was my son and me alone most of the time, and we were fine. I loved every second of it.

We tried for baby number two when our first-born was about two years old, and had our second son when I was twenty-six. Fletcher entered this world with a mop of thick black hair and olive skin. I was in love. I felt so grateful to have experienced an easier birth. My husband was working fewer hours in a new job and so he would be home more. I kept thinking to myself, if I had thrived the first time, surely this time would be even better.

I had a wonderful day in hospital with my little boy. I stayed up all night staring into his eyes and making plans for our future. I promised to love him forever. I whispered that he was the perfect puzzle piece to complete our family and I couldn't wait for morning to come so I could go home and be wrapped up in our love bubble.

I remember so clearly walking through the front door, babe in arms, feeling as though a dark cloud had followed me in, almost as though my soul had left my body. For the first few days, I kept telling myself that I was tired, sore, healing. Fletcher was a very unsettled baby. He cried a lot, and rarely slept. It was tough. He hated the car. He hated being held. He hated being put down. He was growing, he was developing, but I always felt as though something was wrong.

Six months passed and things went from bad to worse. I hadn't told a single soul how much I was struggling. I had no patience. I was not eating. I was living on Panadol and coffee. There were many days where it got so bad that I would sit on the floor of the nursery or the bathroom and cry so much I would vomit. I felt as though I was watching my life from the outside in. My hands shook, I couldn't sleep and my vision was blurry. I constantly felt as though I wanted to run away, but I couldn't escape my body.

Fletcher continued to be unsettled, which did not help. One day, begging him to stop crying, I was holding him in my arms in his room and he was crying so loudly, I could barely think. I looked into his eyes and screamed at him to stop. He cried louder, and I felt my heart break in my chest. I popped him safely in his cot, punched the end of his mattress and walked out of his room. That was the first day I thought about taking my own life.

I so badly wanted to love my baby, but I couldn't. I so badly wanted to scream for help, but I couldn't find the words. I so badly wanted to see with a clear mind, but my world was so cloudy. Noise made my skin crawl. I couldn't piece together anything anymore. I was so lost.

Four weeks passed and I was walking along a main road on my way to work with a coffee, my vision blurred, my heart racing, so close to the traffic that I could feel the draft from the cars. I was seconds away from stepping in front of the traffic when my phone rang. It was Mum. That afternoon I sat with her and Dad and told them how I was feeling. I saw their faces. I saw their worry. I knew I was sick, but I had no idea what it could be.

The next day, the doctor diagnosed me with severe post-natal depression, wrote me a script and immediately put me on a mental health plan. I was in shock.

'What do you mean? I don't want to hurt my baby. I don't want my baby to be taken off me.'

I filled my script the next day and made an appointment with a psychologist. I had a rare reaction to my medication which triggered psychosis. I didn't leave my bedroom for six days. I was taking Valium to sleep and there was someone in my house constantly to make sure I didn't take my own life. I remember lying there and praying I wouldn't wake up. My hands shook, the anxiety was worse, and I felt like a stranger in my own body. I vividly remember staring my husband in the eye and telling him that I was never going to be the same again. Everyone would be better off without me.

On the seventh day, my vision started to clear. Sounds became less overwhelming. My skin started to crawl less. My doctor prescribed an additional medication that took some getting used to, but I slowly rose from the darkness. I saw my therapist weekly for six weeks. I started sleeping. I started smiling. For a moment, a very quick moment, I wondered whether this was the other side. I knew I had a lot of work ahead. I knew it wasn't going to be easy, but I felt as though I could get better.

On the day my son turned twelve months, I fell back in love with him. Post-natal depression had stolen a year of my life, the first year of my life as a mother to Fletcher. I carry so much guilt and some days I still cry thinking about how tough our journey was and how much I missed.

Fletcher is seven now. I am still medicated and take steps EVERY SINGLE DAY to ensure I am looking after my mental health. It's been a commitment, with ups and downs, but I will be forever grateful for the lessons I learnt throughout my battle with mental health. I am a better person, daughter, friend, wife and mother. I learnt more about myself in twelve months than I had my whole life.

Fletcher went on to be diagnosed with autism, ADHD, ODD, anxiety and childhood apraxia of speech. I think, even in my darkness, I knew something was 'different' about him. I used to cry to my mum, telling her, 'Something isn't right.' I used to get told it was my post-natal depression, but I now know even in my darkness that I did love my son, I did know my son and I did feel his soul within my own.

How did you keep swimming?

On my worst days, I would tell myself, 'All you need to do is take ten minutes at a time.' 'Each day I survive is a day closer to feeling brighter.' I used to visualise walking through a long tunnel and every day, I was a little closer to the light at the end.

I would close off to the world and breathe when I felt my heart starting to race, counting to twenty repeatedly until my body relaxed.

You need to do what feels right for you. People would tell me to 'meditate'—I couldn't. People would tell me to 'sleep'—I couldn't. I don't believe there is a one solution fits all.

My therapist told me it was imperative to acknowledge my anxiety. Never ignore it, or it gets louder. Even now, seven years later, when I feel a panic attack coming, I stop and acknowledge the feeling, allow it in and then let it go.

Be kind to yourself. Don't expect more from yourself than you would of a friend going through a similar thing. You are worthy of support. You are worthy of rest. You are worthy of help.

What do you do when you notice your mental health declining?

I have spent so much time trying different things over the last six years to find what works for me.

As a mother, I need and crave the quiet. If I am feeling overwhelmed, the constant noise is really triggering. I have learnt to be honest with my children and tell them, 'Mum needs five minutes, please walk away and I'll come and get you soon.' It's not selfish to set boundaries, even with those dependent upon us.

I have let go of my ego, and I ask for help. It takes a village to walk through this crazy thing we call life. Ask for help.

I get back to nature. I set an alarm for 6 am daily and go for a 5km walk, alone. Exercise and music have saved my life. I dance, a lot.

I get enough sleep (children permitting).

My mental health is the most important thing to me. If I am struggling, it affects everyone.

I am important. You are important.

What advice would you give to someone struggling with their mental health?

As clichéd as it may sound, 'It will get better.' I couldn't believe that a feeling this deep, dark and debilitating could EVER go away or get better. But I promise it does.

The hardest part is asking for help, the second hardest part is accepting it without conditions. The third hardest part is being patient; it won't happen overnight, there will be setbacks, but before you know it, the setbacks will become fewer—that's a promise!

Find a community you trust. In my darkest days, there were no Instagram pages, or other women who were willing to be open and talk about their journey. I was isolated and felt so alone. I have openly shared my story for years, purely because I don't ever want another mother or father to feel like their darkness is theirs alone. Find your tribe. Listen. Learn. Share.

YOU must work on your mental health every day. Help is there, of course, but you are the captain of your own ship.

Medication is not for everyone, but if it's for you, take it and don't let anyone tell you it's wrong!

A good therapist (especially in the early days) is as important as medication, water, toilet paper and breathing. I am not joking!

Don't walk the same road as someone else because it worked for them. Read, listen and educate yourself and then find what works for YOU.

Don't ever fear your mental health. There is no shame in struggling. There is no shame in a diagnosis.

If you're reading this as a parent who was diagnosed with post-natal depression, please always remember:

YOU ARE A WONDERFUL MOTHER

YOU ARE A WONDERFUL FATHER

YOU DID NOT FAIL YOUR BABY

YOU ARE THE PERFECT PARENT FOR YOUR CHILD

IT WAS NOT YOUR FAULT

YOUR BABY LOVES YOU WITH EVERYTHING THEY HAVE

You won't ever get that time back, but I promise the lessons, the love, the patience and the strength you will get from your darkest day will be worth more than every day you lost.

IT'S OKAY TO NOT BE EVERYTHING TO EVERYONE

If you look back at your past,
do so with kind eyes.

KIND EYES

I am so guilty of looking back at my past and resenting the person I used to be. I used to hold so much anger towards myself because I wished I had acted differently, spoke up more when I knew something wasn't right, stood up for myself, said no with conviction, and stayed strong in my own beliefs and values.

There was a series of events that happened during my time in Defence. In the years following, I would replay everything about what had happened in my mind. I started to hate myself for not having walked away sooner when staying was breaking me apart. I was furious at myself for not continuing to fight for what was right when I knew deep down it wasn't okay. I tried once, but I was shut down, and so I stopped. I did not have the strength to keep going.

I remember breaking down in tears as I explained this anger and hatred for my past to my psychologist, who, if you haven't picked up by now, played a huge part in my recovery. She said, 'How could you expect to have acted any differently if you didn't have the tools and knowledge that you do now? Who you are now is completely different from who you were then.'

I thought about that for a moment and then realised how very true that statement was. I am not the same person I used to be. It is as if every stage of my life has been lived by a completely different version of me. My current version of self might have acted differently because I have that knowledge now, but back then, I didn't. By acknowledging that I was only doing the best with what I knew at the time, I was able to free myself of the hate and anger that I had held onto for so long.

Now when I look back at my past, I look back with kind eyes. The more I think about it, the more I want to give those past versions of myself all my love and support. They were doing the very best with what they knew at the time. Those past versions of me are a part of my story, and they have helped to shape the person I am today, as well as the person I will become tomorrow.

HOW TO KEEP SWIMMING

You don't know what you don't know. So, when you look back at your past, remember that you were doing the best you could with the tools and knowledge you had at the time.

Instead of looking back at your past with regret or resentment, look back with kindness, and gently learn the lessons it may present. Ask yourself what this is teaching you. Your past has brought you to this present moment, and you can use what you learnt to shape your future.

Human connection is one of the most valuable tools we have. We often forget how powerful the simple gestures in life can be.

(SMILE) AT THE NEXT PERSON YOU PASS ON YOUR MORNING WALK

ASK THE STAFF AT THE CHECKOUT HOW THEY ARE DOING AND (GENUINELY) BE INTERESTED IN THEIR ANSWER

SAY HELLO TO THE HOMELESS PERSON ON THE STREET AND ACKNOWLEDGE THEIR (PRESENCE)

(THANK) YOUR BUS DRIVER FOR THEIR TIME AND WISH THEM A GOOD DAY

All of these things are free, they take little energy and they have the power to completely change someone's day.

When I've had rough days, it has often been when someone has said hello or started a genuine conversation that has really turned things around for me.

We don't have to walk this earth alone. Spend some time connecting with those around you. We can all find a way to navigate this crazy thing called life together.

'I became my best,
at my worst'

@pharrell_shaymar

Pharrell Shaymar

PHARRELL IS A PROFESSIONAL BOXING COACH, SO YOU WOULD EXPECT THAT HE HAS ENDURED SOME INCREDIBLY TOUGH FIGHTS. YET FOR PHARRELL, NONE OF THOSE FIGHTS COULD EVER COMPARE TO THE LIFELONG BATTLE HE HAS HAD WITH HIS OWN MIND. USING HIS LIVED EXPERIENCE, PHARRELL IS NOW FIGHTING TO MAKE A DIFFERENCE FOR TRANS AND NON-BINARY PEOPLE IN COMBAT SPORTS.

I was just five years old when I first recognised that something wasn't right. Every day I would wake up in a female's body, knowing deep down that this body was not mine. I knew I was supposed to be a male.

How do you comprehend life as it is when you don't know who you are and can't change who you are? This is how I fell into depression, self-harm and not wanting to be here anymore.

Navigating school is never easy, kids can be cruel, but it wasn't the kids who hurt me the most. It was the teachers throughout both primary and high school that destroyed my confidence, my mentality and my emotional state. I was singled out by teachers, one in particular saying, 'You're a girl, not a boy.' Can you imagine standing in front of your classmates and being told by someone in a position of power that you are wrong to be expressing who you are at your core?

This same teacher forced me to leave school at fourteen and called other schools to let them know about me before I had a chance to show them the real me. Because of this, I wasn't welcome at any other schools. At the mere age of fourteen, my school life had finished through no fault of my own.

I spent years on my own, in my room, crying, depressed, praying. There was so much going on that dying felt like the best option.

I have spent my whole life questioning, fighting, crying, wishing, dreaming and wanting this male body.

I have spent my whole life walking two lines on a path that never went in the direction I wanted.

I have spent my whole life never knowing if today would be my last day on earth. I didn't know how to live another day not knowing if I could look at myself in the mirror when I was struggling to accept myself.

To be a man, but be born a woman. To know I am a male, but born biologically a female, growing into a person I don't resonate with.

My mother gave up her life to support me and my sister. She was always left with no money, no car, no support and no one to guide her where I was concerned. My mother adores me, and with the little resources she had, she took me to anyone who could support me in starting the process for my transition.

But with so little support, each day I self-harmed, marking lines in my arm of the numbers 16, 18 and 21. These were the ages I was told I had to wait before I could transition. I was eighteen before I was finally given the green light by medical professionals to begin transitioning into the man I always knew I was.

I had scars, burns and bruises on my body marking the pain and trauma of broken promises from medical professionals. I used medication to overdose. Death became the light into leaving a world that no longer made sense.

Throughout my childhood, I believed I was the cause of my family's sadness and a burden to those around me. The guilt and the inner voice telling me my existence caused more harm than good haunted me for twenty-five years.

Now, I am finally aware that I was a broken human because of verbal abuse. I suffered mental anguish from repeated comments about my unworthiness. I suffered physical pain from being thrown into walls, or against the floor, hitting my head until I could no longer think. I was conditioned to be hurt.

My mother saved me. She shared her love for me every day, giving me another day of hope. She is the reason I am who I am today. She taught me that gender doesn't define us, but diverts us from who we truly are. Although I will never become a biological male, I am the person my mother raised me to be, a gentleman.

I now love who I am, because I am everything that I wanted to be as a young girl. I am now a man of truth, a man of love, a man of passion, a man of courage and a man of drive.

I am also a woman of art, a woman of secrecy, a woman of softness, a woman of strength and a woman of purity.

How did you keep swimming?

I found a sport that gave me a mirror to see into, to start seeing the reflections around me, all the voices I was listening to, the images of those pushing me to become someone I was not. I found boxing.

Boxing gave me a platform to stand on and helped me to face myself. Boxing helped me battle the pain I felt with the image in the mirror. Through boxing I was able to stand up against the one person who could win; myself.

Boxing taught me to move.

Boxing taught me to find steps in a different direction away from the battle I was fighting.

Boxing taught me no matter how small the ring may be, and how big my opponent is, I can move around the ring, I can slip into a side step that I can change direction in, I can use the ropes to bounce off and cut my angle in another direction.

Each movement is another step forward in my ring.

Each slip is another tool I use to respond.

Each punch thrown at me no longer reached me, as I developed a way to move around my ring by facing myself, by using my tools, and winning my bout.

Boxing showed me how to keep fighting so I could continue to win the fight against my mind.

In my life I've spent a lot of time not being able to think. There have been times when I could not find the energy to leave my bed, or even speak. Situations were hard because they were out of my control. I had no understanding of how to accept what was happening to me when I didn't understand why I was here. But even when I had lost the drive to survive, I felt deep down that I was more than I knew, that I deserved more, and I would not let anyone or anything keep me from becoming more. I wanted to leave this world, but there was a stronger feeling that I do belong here and my time isn't up.

At a time in my life when I lost everything—my relationship, my job, my finances, my mental health and my emotional wellbeing—I kept going and at my worst, I became my best.

What did you do when you noticed your mental health declining?

I spoke to my mother, she is my best friend. No matter what I said, how bad it was, how depressed I was or how sad my words were, she listened to me with an open heart and never made me feel any less. She never told me what to do, how to be, or how to feel. She just listened and would always tell me something positive about myself, reminding me of my passion, my drive, the positive qualities in me, and guiding me to keep at least one positive thing in my mind.

I talked to my best friend. I wasn't open with her about my mental health, but I told her about the hardest time in my life. Like my mother, she let me speak, acknowledged how I felt in a respectful way, didn't judge or tell me how to act. She treated me as she's always treated me and if anything she showed me more love.

I started seeing a counsellor who also did reiki. I trusted her and opened up to her. Even though she could see the positive bigger picture, she always allowed me to find my own way in my own time. She gave me unconditional support, never judged, never pushed me, never pressured me, and always tried to give me another perspective, or encouraged me to try another approach to help me see things differently, because I couldn't even see what was in front of me.

All these simple things supported me significantly, and I needed support, not to be told what to do, or how to be.

What advice would you give to someone struggling with their mental health?

Don't be hard on yourself.

Don't feel you need listen to everyone's advice or opinions. When you are struggling, it is personal.

Focus on yourself and understand that your feelings are valid.

Understand where your emotions are coming from. It's like tracing them back to find something you've lost!

This is a time for discovering your strengths, your abilities and your way. Everyone has their own strengths and it is in these times that you will find yours.

A new hobby may suit you, like writing, walking, going to new places, a sport, an art, nature, meditation, new adventures.

Even when you don't feel like doing anything, when motivation is a challenge, there are always a few minutes where you can find your drive for something and be inspired by it. Those few minutes become longer and longer. Time seems to go slowly, but taking the time for yourself is loving yourself.

There is a song I play (Get Lost—Ford remix, by Bearson) whose lyrics mean you get lost to find yourself and that although you feel lost, you are finding yourself.

Only you know who you are.

For the times you may not, which may be more often than not, pause and take your time.

You may feel lost, but you are only finding yourself.

You may feel down, but that's only because you're struggling to find a reason to look up.

Let a friend, a loved one, or someone dear to you take your hand. Let them help you. Or maybe you can take your own hand. Step by step, nothing big, just small steps.

You don't need to look up, just look forward.

ASK YOURSELF WHAT DO YOU LIKE?

WHAT MAKES YOU SMILE?

WHAT DO YOU ADMIRE?

WHAT GIVES YOU A REASON TO TAKE ONE STEP?

Try to rediscover who you are.

It's okay if you don't have the answer.

If you can just take one step forward, when you look back you'll have stepped a thousand reasons away from who you once were and into the person you want to run with.

I pulled out the weeds,

Heaved and tugged,

Then raked the dirt over.

In freshly turned soil,

I planted new seeds.

I nurtured and tended to them,

Until one day,

I bloomed.

LAURY HOUGHTON

SHAKE IT OFF

When I was nineteen, I used to coach tennis. There was a three-year-old girl enrolled in one of my classes. At such a young age, hitting the balls I threw to her seemed like an impossible task. I don't blame her. When you're only three, it's hard to figure out the world, let alone a sport.

Every week, she would show up to the lessons and try to hit the balls without any success. The other kids were older and bigger than she was, and they didn't struggle as much. Slowly, her excitement started to fade away.

It was the last lesson of the term, and I could see her energy had changed from when she first started. She was feeling the pressure to be successful. She was feeling disappointment, and I could see she was struggling with those feelings internally.

When it was her turn to hit the ball, I put down my racquet and asked her to put down hers. I said, 'Let's just shake it off.'

Together, we stood on the court and took a moment to shake all those negative thoughts and feelings away. We were waving our arms and kicking our legs. We looked silly, and we were having fun. Her smile started to widen. Then I asked if she was ready, and she ever-so-confidently said, 'Yep.'

I threw her the ball, and in one effortless motion, she hit her first tennis ball. I screamed and celebrated. She was beaming and jumping up and down. Her excitement came rushing back and joy filled her soul once again.

111

HOW TO KEEP SWIMMING

This is such a simple story, but it's an incredibly important reminder that when it all gets too much, when you start to feel the pressure, when you are struggling with your surroundings or the expectations placed on you, just shake it off. Take a moment and literally move your body in all directions. Get the negative energy moving through and out of your body. Once you feel ready and that energy has started to clear out, try again.

There are always trials and tribulations in life, but if we take the time to listen to ourselves and what we need, our next move might just be the one that makes it all worth it.

"THE HEALTHY AND STRONG INDIVIDUAL
IS THE ONE WHO ASKS FOR HELP
WHEN HE NEEDS IT, WHETHER HE'S
GOT AN ABSCESS ON HIS KNEE OR IN
HIS SOUL"

RONA BARRETT

MENTAL HEALTH HELPLINES

Is it an emergency? If you or someone you know is at immediate risk of harm, call triple zero (000).

24/7 SUPPORT HELPLINES

Suicide Callback Service—Anyone at risk of suicide, concerned about someone at risk, bereaved by suicide or experiencing emotional or mental health issues
Phone: 1300 659 467
Website: suicidecallbackservice.org.au

Lifeline—Anyone experiencing a personal crisis
Phone: 13 11 14
Website: lifeline.org.au

Beyond Blue—Anyone feeling anxious or depressed
Phone: 1300 22 4636
Website: beyondblue.org.au

MensLine Australia—Men with emotional or relationship concerns
Phone: 1300 76 99 78
Website: mensline.org.au

Kids Helpline—Counselling for young people aged five to twenty-five
Phone: 1800 55 1800
Website: kidshelpline.com.au

Open Arms—Veterans and families counselling
Phone: 1800 011 046
Website: openarms.gov.au

1800RESPECT—Support for people affected by sexual assault, domestic or family violence and abuse
Phone: 1800 737 732
Website: 1800respect.org.au

SUPPORT HELPLINES (NOT 24/7)

Blue Knot Foundation Helpline—Empowering recovery from complex trauma
Phone: 1300 657 380 (9 am–5 pm, seven days a week AEST)
Website: blueknot.org.au

Butterfly Foundation's National Helpline—People with eating disorders, and body image and related issues
Phone: 1800 33 4673 (8 am–midnight, seven days a week AEST)
Website: butterfly.org.au

eheadspace—Support and counselling for young people aged twelve to twenty-five and their families and friends
Phone: 1800 650 890 (9 am–1 am, seven days a week AEST)
Website: headspace.org.au/eheadspace

FriendLine—Anyone who needs to reconnect or just wants a chat
Phone: 1800 424 287 (10 am–8 pm, seven days a week AEST)
Website: friendline.org.au

QLife—LGBTI peer support and referral for people wanting to talk about sexuality, identity, gender, bodies, feelings or relationships
Phone: 1800 184 527 (3 pm–midnight, seven days a week AEST)
Website: qlife.org.au

PANDA—Support for women, men and families affected by anxiety and depression during pregnancy and in the first year of parenthood
Phone: 1300 726 306 (9 am–7.30 pm, Monday-Friday AEST/AEDT)
Website: panda.org.au

SANE Australia—Anyone in Australia affect by complex mental health issues
Phone: 1800 18 7263 (10 am–10 pm, Monday-Friday AEST)
Website: sane.org

Thank you to those who held space for me when I couldn't hold myself up. Thank you to those who found me when I was losing myself. Thank you to those who brought light to my life in the midst of my darkness. You know who you are. You have continued to accept every version of me, and for that, I am forever grateful.

Thank you to my psychologist, Michelle. You saw me, you understood me and you turned my life around. I am a different person today, a stronger person, for having met you.

Thank you to Ash. Your mentoring and support truly helped guide me in the right direction so *Keep Swimming* could be born. I appreciate you.

Thank you to the illustrator, Ceri. You tranformed my words into the magical illustrations found on these pages. I will always cherish the time we spent working together in tropical Sri Lanka. Thank you for everything.

Thank you to the book designer, Vero. You listened to my dream for this book and through your incredible design work and passion for the project, you turned it into a reality. I can not thank you enough.

Thank you to the editor, Gail. Your ability to work with the words in this book and make it flow so beautifully left me speechless. Working with you was an absolute pleasure.

Thank you to the photographer, Marie. Your photographs allow the readers to be transported to a place of peace and calm. Thank you for sharing your beautiful work with me.

To the writers in this book, thank you from the bottom of my heart. I will never have enough words to truly express my gratitude for connecting with you and for your willingness to share your story. With your words, you are changing the narrative and the stigma of mental health. Through your voice, you are giving others hope. This book is only possible because of you.

THANK YOU

Everybody has a voice and everybody has a story.

If you feel called to share yours, please email
hello@keepswimmingbook.com

I would absolutely love to hear from you.

Annaleise x

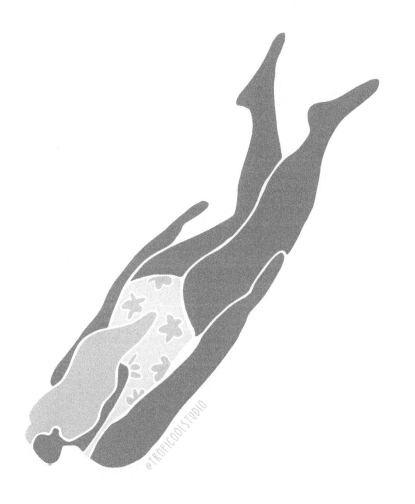

@TROPICOOLSTUDIO

ABOUT THE ILLUSTRATOR

CERI IS PASSIONATELY LIVING AS A FULL TIME ILLUSTRATOR, SURFER AND
TRAVELLER. CERI IMMERSES HERSELF IN COASTAL COMMUNITIES, WHERE SHE
CAN BE SURROUNDED BY THE ONE THING THAT BRINGS HER TO HER TRUEST
SELF - THE OCEAN. THE ILLUSTRATIONS WITHIN THIS BOOK ARE INSPIRED BY
CERI'S DEEP LOVE OF WATER, HER APPRECIATION FOR SLOW LIVING AND HER
PASSION FOR GIVING OTHERS A SENSE OF CALM AND HOPE THROUGH HER ART.

Ingram Content Group UK Ltd.
Milton Keynes UK
UKHW020801110623
423185UK00002B/28